Recent Researches in the Music
of the Nineteenth and
Early Twentieth Centuries
Volume 17

Charles-Marie Widor

THE SYMPHONIES FOR ORGAN

Symphonie VII

Edited by John R. Near

A-R Editions, Inc.

THE SYMPHONIES
FOR ORGAN

RECENT RESEARCHES IN THE MUSIC OF THE NINETEENTH AND EARLY TWENTIETH CENTURIES

Rufus Hallmark, general editor

A-R Editions, Inc., publishes seven series of musicological editions that present music brought to light in the course of current research:

Recent Researches in the Music of the Middle Ages and Early Renaissance
Charles Atkinson, general editor

Recent Researches in the Music of the Renaissance
James Haar, general editor

Recent Researches in the Music of the Baroque Era
Christoph Wolff, general editor

Recent Researches in the Music of the Classical Era
Eugene K. Wolf, general editor

Recent Researches in the Music of the Nineteenth and Early Twentieth Centuries
Rufus Hallmark, general editor

Recent Researches in American Music
H. Wiley Hitchcock, general editor

Recent Researches in the Oral Traditions of Music
Philip V. Bohlman, general editor

Each *Recent Researches* edition is devoted to works
by a single composer or to a single genre of composition.
The contents are chosen for their potential interest to scholars
and performers, then prepared for publication according to the
standards that govern the making of all reliable historical editions.

Subscribers to any of these series, as well as patrons of subscribing institutions,
are invited to apply for information about the "Copyright-Sharing Policy"
of A-R Editions, Inc., under which policy any part of an edition
may be reproduced free of charge for study or performance.

For information contact

A-R EDITIONS, INC.
801 Deming Way
Madison, Wisconsin 53717

(608) 836-9000

RECENT RESEARCHES IN THE MUSIC OF THE NINETEENTH
AND EARLY TWENTIETH CENTURIES • VOLUME 17

Charles-Marie Widor

THE SYMPHONIES FOR ORGAN

Symphonie VII

Edited by John R. Near

A-R Editions, Inc.
Madison

Charles-Marie Widor
THE SYMPHONIES FOR ORGAN

Edited by John R. Near

*Recent Researches in the Music
of the Nineteenth and Early Twentieth Centuries*

Opus 13	Symphonie I	in C Minor	Volume 11
	Symphonie II	in D Major	Volume 12
	Symphonie III	in E Minor	Volume 13
	Symphonie IV	in F Minor	Volume 14
Opus 42	Symphonie V	in F Minor	Volume 15
	Symphonie VI	in G Minor	Volume 16
	Symphonie VII	in A Minor	Volume 17
	Symphonie VIII	in B Major	Volume 18
Opus 70	*Symphonie gothique*		Volume 19
Opus 73	*Symphonie romane*		Volume 20

© 1994 by A-R Editions, Inc.
All rights reserved
Printed in the United States of America

Library of Congress Cataloging-in-Publication Data

Widor, Charles Marie, 1844–1937.
 [Symphonies, organ, no. 7, op. 42, no. 3, A minor]
 Symphonie VII / edited by John R. Near.
 p. of music. —(The symphonies for organ / Charles-Marie Widor)
 (Recent researches in the music of the nineteenth and early
 twentieth centuries, ISSN 0193-5364 ; v. 17)
 "The original French editions and copies of these with
 corrections and emendations in Widor's hand form the basis
 for this critical edition"—P. vii.
 ISBN 0-89579-286-9
 1. Symphonies (Organ) I. Near, John Richard, 1947–
II. Series. III. Series: Widor, Charles Marie, 1844–1937.
Symphonies, organ (A-R Editions)
M2.R23834   vol. 17
[M8]   93-48055
                                          CIP
                                           M

Contents

INTRODUCTION
   The Sources   vii
   Editorial Policies   viii
   Widor's Registrations   ix
   Critical Commentary   ix

WIDOR'S *AVANT-PROPOS*   xvi

PLATES   xix

SYMPHONIE VII IN A MINOR
   I   3
   II. Choral   13
   III   21
   IV   31
   V   41
   VI. Finale   45

APPENDIX 1
   I. Editions *B* and *B'*, Mm. 160–68. *Emend*-1 sketch, Mm. 161–68   61

APPENDIX 2
   IV. Version *B/B'*   62

APPENDIX 3
   IV. Edition *C*, Mm. 108–32   76

APPENDIX 4
   V. Editions *B* and *B'*   78

APPENDIX 5
   V. Edition *C*, Mm. 38–50   82

APPENDIX 6
   VI. Finale. Version *B/B'*, Mm. 235–305   83

Widor, 1890. Oil portrait by Charles-Auguste-Émile Durand (1837–1917), known as Carolus-Duran. Location unknown. Himself an amateur musician, Carolus-Duran painted many Parisian musician friends, including Gounod and Pasdeloup. His portraits were known for their truthful appearance and for the influence of his favorite master, Velázquez. Carolus-Duran painted Widor from the vantage point of a close friend, and the portrait bespeaks the alert personality of the composer.
Photographic reproduction courtesy of the Widor family

Introduction

From the time of their first publication, the organ symphonies of Charles-Marie Widor (1844–1937) have been recognized as masterpieces. Their influence on subsequent organ literature was once immense. As new generations of organ music became popular, however, there inevitably came a time when Widor's symphonies were neglected, often being judged outmoded. Even the French Romantic organ, perfected by Cavaillé-Coll and adored by musicians, was abused by later generations. Sufficient time was required to pass before Widor's art and instrument could be considered from a fresh and independent musical perspective. That perspective has evidently been achieved, for in recent years increasing numbers of musicians have begun evaluating the symphonies on their own terms, with the result that the works have enjoyed a notable resurgence of popularity. At the same time, the French Romantic organ has regained its former status.

Widor was perhaps his own most demanding critic. Following the first publication of each organ symphony, a continual transformation was effected by the composer through several revisions. In certain cases nearly six decades intervened between first and last versions of a work. Even after the final published edition, Widor continued to scrutinize his organ works, applying finishing touches to the pieces that have constituted his most enduring legacy.

This comprehensive edition of Widor's ten organ symphonies is the first to incorporate the many final emendations made by the composer in his own copies. Here also are presented for the first time together substantially or completely different earlier versions of passages, sections, and complete movements as they were conceived by Widor in the course of his long career. Using information in the Critical Commentary and the music of the Appendixes, musicians can perform or study these several earlier versions of each work.

The Preface to this edition (vol. 11, Symphonie I) provides a full discussion of the symphonies' genesis and historical environment as well as an extended discussion of editorial policy, sources, and performance. In this Introduction are provided information on performance sufficient to give the reader a sense of Widor's own preferences in registration and expression (including a translation of his foreword, or *avant-propos*), a conspectus of the sources, a summary of editorial policy, and a Critical Commentary.

The Sources

The original French editions and copies of these with corrections and emendations in Widor's hand form the basis for this critical edition. The locations of Widor's original holographs, if extant, are unknown. After extensively researching these works, the editor believes that all editions have surfaced, with one possible exception, noted in the Preface. These are listed here together with the identifying abbreviations used in the Critical Commentary and Appendixes. (More complete information on the sources appears in the Preface to the present edition.)

A	The first edition of opus 13, Symphonies I–IV, published in Paris in 1872 by the firm of J. Maho.
A'	A subsequent issue of *A* with minuscule alterations, published in 1879 by the firm of J. Hamelle together with the first editions of Symphonies V and VI.
B	The first complete issue of opus 42, comprising Symphonies V–VIII, together with the first major revision of opus 13, published in Paris in 1887 by Hamelle.
B'	A subsequent issue of *B* with small revisions to Symphonies I, VI, VII, and VIII, released between 1888 and 1892.
C	A new edition of opuses 13 and 42 (excepting Symphonie VI), published in 1901 and bearing the heading "New edition, revised, and entirely modified by the composer (1900–1901)."
C'	A subsequent issue of *C* that includes a new version of Symphonie VI and revisions to Symphonies I–V and VII–VIII, released by 1911.
D	A new edition of opuses 13 and 42, published in 1920, bearing the heading "New edition, revised, and entirely modified by the composer (1914–1918), (1920)."
E	The final published edition, again with revisions, issued 1928–29.
Emend 1	A copy of *B'* apparently used by Widor while preparing the revisions of edition *C* but also containing other emendations.
Emend 2	A bound and complete collection of single symphonies (representing variously the versions of editions *D* or *E*) with emendations made by Widor mostly after 1929, the year of edition *E*.
Emend 3	A copy of Symphonie V in the version of edition *D*, with numerous emendations by the composer, dated October 1927 in Widor's hand. This copy includes the revisions present

in the 1929 edition, but it also contains further emendations, including some duplicated in *Emend* 2 and arguably entered after 1929.

Schw 5–7 Gunsbach, France, Maison Schweitzer, MO 157, a bound volume of Symphonies V, VI (movement V), and VII (movements I–IV). On the first page of Symphonie V, Schweitzer has signed his name and written, "Cet exemplaire est corrigé à la main par Widor même pour moi" [This copy is corrected in Widor's own hand for me]. These copies represent edition C, except for Symphonie VI (see vol. 16, Symphonie VI, of this edition).

Schw 7–8 Gunsbach, France, Maison Schweitzer, MO 158, a bound volume of Symphonies VII (mvmts. V–VI) and VIII. This copy represents edition C; consequently, the markings do not apply to edition E. An exception occurs in the Finale of the Symphonie VII and is reported in the Critical Notes to that movement.

Riem 7 Berea, Ohio, The Riemenschneider Bach Institute at Baldwin-Wallace College, R 4004, comprises a single copy of Symphonie VII in edition D owned by Albert Riemenschneider, Widor's most illustrious American pupil. Among the many markings are some emendations in ink that appear to be in Widor's hand.

Identical versions of movements in different editions are denoted in the Critical Commentary and the Appendixes by a slash between the identifying letters; for example, A/A'/B/B' means that a movement so identified remains the same through editions A, A', B, and B'.

Editorial Policies

Edition E (or, what amounts to the same thing, a version remaining constant through edition E) is generally taken as the principal source for the main body of this edition. Sources for Appendix variants are identified individually in the Critical Commentary. All departures from the source either are distinguished typographically (when they are editorial and straightforward) or are identified in the Critical Commentary (when they derive from other sources or are not explained by policies described here). There are two exceptions to the policy of bracketing: editorial ties, slurs, hairpins, and directs are dashed; editorial cautionary accidentals appear in reduced size; all other editorial additions are enclosed in brackets.

The original French prints are themselves replete with cautionary accidentals, usually provided to cancel flats and sharps in previous measures. All except repetitious cautionary accidentals within a measure are preserved in this edition.

In the Critical Commentary the three staves of a system are indexed 1, 2, and 3, in order from top to bottom. Occasionally staff 1 in the source editions is congested, while an empty or nearly empty staff lies directly below. In such contexts this edition sometimes tacitly transfers left-hand voices to the open staff 2.

In the sources, indications of dynamics under staff 1 are sometimes duplicated under staves 2 or 3 or both in contexts where the Pédale and other manuals would have to share those dynamics in any event. The editor has suppressed most of these redundant dynamic indications. In addition, the old engravings frequently place dynamic indications over staff 1 because of space limitations on the page; conversely, they sometimes place tempo indications between staves 1 and 2 for the same reason. This edition tacitly regularizes the position of all such marks, putting dynamic indications within the system and tempo indications above it. There is an obvious exception to this rule: namely, when a dynamic is meant to apply to one staff alone, it appears closest to the affected voice(s)—therefore, sometimes above staff 1. Because Widor indicated registration and dynamics somewhat differently in editions A and A', the source placement of the relevant signs is preserved in appendix extracts from them.

Widor indicated staccato with the dot up to the late 1890s, but he favored the wedge thereafter. The two signs become mixed in passages partially revised by the composer after about 1900 (the period of edition C). Widor's pedagogical works on organ music reveal that both signs had the same significance for him. In the present edition all wedges are tacitly changed to dots in pieces conceived before Widor's change of orthography; wedges are retained in movements composed after the change.

Beaming in the original French editions is sometimes used to clarify phrasing. Beaming in the new edition follows that of the sources except when, under certain stringent conditions spelled out in detail in the Preface to this edition (see vol. 11, Symphonie I), it can be shown with great probability that inconsistencies arise through oversight or through adherence to an outmoded convention for beaming.

Characteristic of Widor's musical orthography is its attention to inner contrapuntal voices in every musical texture. At times this leads to a phalanx of stems all aiming for the same metrical position. Stemming in the new edition generally follows that of the sources, since the appearance of counterpoint, even in predominantly homophonic textures, conveys much of the "feel" and attitude proper to Widor's symphonies. Departures from the source are made only in clearly defined circumstances spelled out in detail in the Preface to this edition. In general, the number of voices in a measure is kept constant. In clearly homophonic contexts, where Widor himself is less strict, inconsistencies in the number of voices in a measure are usually allowed to stand. All editorial rests are bracketed. Stems added by analogy with parallel or closely similar passages are not bracketed, but the source reading is reported in a critical note. All other stems added to clarify inconsistent voicing are bracketed. Infrequently, superfluous rests or stems in the sources are tacitly removed to keep part writing consistent in a measure.

In conformity with accepted practice of that era, the original French editions of Widor's organ symphonies provide double barlines for all changes of key and for some changes of meter. In this edition these are converted to single barlines unless there is also a new tempo, a new texture, or some other sign of a structural subdivision.

Reference to pitch in the Critical Commentary is made as follows: middle C = c'; C above middle C = c"; C below middle C = c; two octaves below middle C = C. Successive pitches are separated by commas, simultaneous pitches by virgules.

Widor's Registrations

Widor generally indicated registrations by family of tone-color instead of exact stop nomenclature. In so doing he never intended to condone willful or indiscriminate interpretations of his registrational plans. He had a particular horror of kaleidoscopic stop changes and artlessly haphazard use of the Expression pedal. To those who indulged in a continual manipulation of the stops or Expression pedal, he habitually advised, "I beg you, no magic lantern effects." Barring the unfortunate necessity of making certain adaptations to varying organs, one should no more alter the "orchestration" of a Widor organ symphony than change or dress up the instrumentation of a Beethoven symphony. Clearly, the faithful realization of Widor's registrational plan is essential to the presentation of these works as the composer heard them. Beyond this, knowledge of the Cavaillé-Coll organ, the instrument preferred by Widor, will also prove useful to the performer intent on maximum fidelity to the composer's intention. A discussion of this organ and its constraints on performance can be found in the Preface to this edition (see vol. 11, Symphonie I).

To indicate the registration he wanted, Widor adopted a relatively simple shorthand system: **G** represents Grand-orgue (Great); **P** Positif (Positive); **R** Récit (Swell); **Péd.** Pédale (Pedal). Fonds are the foundation stops; Anches the chorus reed stops as well as all correlative stops included in the Jeux de combinaison. Pitch designations are self-evident.

When found above, within, or directly below the keyboard staves, a single letter instructs the organist to play on that particular uncoupled manual. When two or three letters are combined in these locations, the first designates the manual to play on, the second and subsequent letters what is to be coupled to it. For example, **GPR** instructs the organist to play on the Grand-orgue with the Positif and Récit coupled to it; **PR** tells one to play on the Positif with the Récit coupled to it; and so on.

When found under the lowest staff, one or more letters designate which manuals are to be coupled to the Pédale. When Widor employs only a dynamic marking in the course of the Pédale line, the performer should determine at his own discretion which Pédale coupler needs to be retired or reintroduced.

All crescendo and decrescendo indications, no matter how lengthy, are to be effected only by manipulation of the Expression pedal, unless the crescendo leads to a *fff*. In that case the Jeux de combinaison of each division are to be brought into play successively on strong beats: first those of the Récit (perhaps already on), then those of the Positif (sometimes indicated with a *ff*), and finally those of the Grand-orgue and Pédale on the *fff*. For the decrescendo they are to be retired in reverse order on weak beats.

Critical Commentary

Symphonies VII and VIII, like the two preceding symphonies, can be paired aesthetically. They appear to have been composed in close succession, and they were published together in 1887. In a letter dated "10 avril 87" to Alexander Wilhelm Gottschalg, an organist and director of the newspaper *Urania* in Weimar, Widor writes:

> In a few days the last two symphonies and the new edition of the first four, corrected and considerably augmented, will appear. I wanted to balance these first works and to give them the amplitude of the following ones. The whole is at the engraver Röder in Leipzig. I will send them to you as soon as possible in the hope that they will interest you, in spite of their mysticism and severity at first sight.*

In these latest works Widor advanced a new, more complex musical language for the organ, one that demands much from both listener and performer. The composer's original concept of symphonic organ music, which included character pieces with an occasional bent toward a sweet salon style, is nowhere in evidence here. These symphonies are fully products for a new age. Emblematic of this new age were the incredible technical innovations and engineering marvels displayed at the Paris Expositions of 1878 (when Widor performed—likely premiered—the G-minor symphony) and 1889 (when he likely premiered the B-minor symphony); 1887 marked the beginning of construction on perhaps the most celebrated symbol of the new era, Gustave Eiffel's tower on the Champs de Mars. In much the same spirit, Cavaillé-Coll was bringing the nineteenth-century organ to its technical and tonal apogee, and it is Widor's symphonies that tapped the resources of the Cavaillé-Coll organ to the fullest. The propelling energy of the first movement of Symphonie VII seems caught up in the quickening human spirit of the times.

Widor's ever-favored Symphonies V and VI, as well as the later, revered *gothique* and *romane*, have almost totally eclipsed the two intervening giants, the longest

---

*Letter in the private collection of the editor.

and weightiest of Widor's organ works. This is indeed unfortunate. Symphonies VII and VIII—arguably the most symphonic of the ten—are not one bit less worthy, only more difficult. As Saint-Saëns wrote to Widor, "the great majority of organists . . . do not have your skills and retreat terrified before your works."* Herein, perhaps, lies the reason for the very real neglect that these symphonies have experienced. From the outset they represented organ music of the future, and until recently most organists seemed unable to grasp them. One can only conjecture about the reception they might have received had they been scored for orchestra. It is noteworthy that as Widor composed Symphonies VII and VIII, two Teutonic colleagues were completing similarly substantial masterpieces in the orchestral genre: Bruckner, Symphonies VII and VIII; and Brahms, Symphonies III and IV. Of course, Widor also shared with Bruckner the tendency to revise; his six-movement Symphonie VII exists in five versions: B, B', C, C'/D, and E.

I

It is probably this movement that Madame Widor referred to when she wrote to Albert Schweitzer on 20 January 1939:

> The Allegro of the Seventh Symphony was one of the pieces that I heard played most often by Charles-Marie; I can say that my recollections date from the last century because my mother, who preferred Saint-Sulpice to her parish, Sainte-Clotilde, always took me there.†

The jagged, sharply punctuated opening theme exerts a raw power not seen before in Widor's organ music. It is first stated in double octaves (mm. 1–8) and then harmonized over a dominant pedal (mm. 9–16). After a transitional development of this material (moving the tonal center from A to D), a contrasting second theme in even quarter notes is introduced, effectively set in counterpoint above the leaping first theme (mm. 34–45). (This new theme is related to the opening phrase of II. Choral—see especially mm. 40–42.) A more fluid musical idea in sixteenths, adumbrated in measures 17–21 and then recast as the pithy motive in measure 60 (staff 2), completes the germinal material of the movement and functions as the third protagonist in the ensuing drama of this movement's musical development.

The opening registration is given as "Grand-orgue, Positif, Récit, Pédale: Fonds et Anches 4, 8, 16 etc." It is characteristic of Widor in big, tutti movements to specify the registration in general terms rather than with fussy specifics; he assumes the performer will take care of the details, and here the abbreviation "etc." is especially telling. Whereas Widor often employs abbreviations of manual directives, in this movement—surprisingly, since the intent of terraced dynamics is quite clear—complete directives appear: **GPR, PR, R**.

---

*Lettres adressées à Widor de Saint-Saëns, Ms 4123, no. 54 (dated 29 Sept. 1919) Institut de France, Paris.
†Gunsbach, France, Maison Schweitzer, Correspondance, Widor à Schweitzer.

Only in measure 79, staff 2, is there apparently an intentional use of **P** to signify "solo."

There are only a few differences between the four versions of this movement: B, B', C/C'/D, and E. For the present edition, E is the principal source.

As noted in the commentaries for earlier symphonies, Widor sometimes repeatedly revised the same passage. In this movement it was measures 161–68; these differ in editions B, B', and C—the reading of edition C remaining through edition E. In addition, there is a sketch in *Emend* 1 that appears to present an intermediary step between editions B' and C. To show the development of Widor's thought in this passage, the readings of editions B and B' as well as of the *Emend*-1 sketch are given as Appendix 1.

In other parts of the movement, earlier versions and edition E are nearly identical. For edition E Widor deleted the staccato articulation from one passage and revised the rhythm and articulation in another. This latter revision was so badly muddled by the engraver that edition E is metrically unintelligible in those measures: the edition-E figurations conflate the rhythm of the earlier reading with that of Widor's emendation. Fortunately, Widor penned the correct reading into *Emend* 2—see the Critical Notes below and plate 1, which reproduces the pertinent systems of *Emend* 2.

CRITICAL NOTES

M. 25, when effecting the registration directive, it is unimportant when the Grand-orgue Anches are suppressed, but the Positif Anches should be suppressed on beat 1, or perhaps even as early as m. 24, beat 3, so that the swell shutters can be closed, as indicated, during beat 1.   Mm. 26, 28, 30, 31, staff 1, beat 3 has sixteenth chord slurred to sixteenth chord, thirty-second rest, staccato thirty-second chord—not only do these durations not add up to a full beat, but the voices of staves 1 and 2 are misaligned in m. 26, and the articulation marks are misplaced in m. 31 (beat 2, the eighth chord is slurred to the first beat-3 sixteenth chord, and the second beat-3 sixteenth chord is staccato); the present edition follows *Emend* 2; from these emendations one can see that Widor had meant to revise these beats in edition E to match the rhythm and articulation of similar figures in mm. 27 and 29 (see also the report for m. 116).   M. 32, staff 3, editorial extension of the slur follows phrasing in mm. 14 and 174—here the staccato notes of staves 1 and 2 contrast with the slurred staff-3 note.   M. 34, staff 1, beat 2 has no outgoing slur in any edition—an error; the editorial slur follows the implication of m. 35, which begins a new page in the source and shows an incoming slur.

M. 71, staff 2, beat 1, g'/g" are stemmed together—the separate stemming in this edition conforms to the voicing elsewhere in the measure.   M. 73, staff 1, upper voice, note 3 has no dot in any edition—an error; beat 3, the notes are stemmed together—the separate stemming in this edition conforms to the voicing elsewhere in the measure; staff 2, beat 3, the notes are stemmed together—the separate stemming in this edition conforms to the voicing elsewhere in the measure. M. 94, staff 1, beat 3, note has no downstem in any edition—edition follows analogous m. 90.

M. 116, staff 1, beat 2 has the only remaining instance of the rhythm Widor systematically revised in mm. 26, 28, 30, and 31—it is not unlikely that its presence escaped Widor's attention during the process of revision; if that is true, then this figuration should be played as two slurred sixteenth dyads, sixteenth rest, sixteenth dyad. M. 156, the *fff* marks are located at m. 157, beat 1, in all editions.

Version *C/C'/D* differs from edition *E* as follows. Mm. 26, 28, 30, and 31, staff 1, beat 3 is staccato eighth chord, staccato sixteenth chord, thirty-second rest, staccato thirty-second chord (also in editions *B* and *B'*)—the editor finds the contrast between the rhythm in these measures and that of mm. 27 and 29 to be very effective. M. 79, staff 3, note 2, through m. 84, note 1, all notes are staccato. (M. 132, staff 2, beat 2, dyad changed to triad with added d in *Emend* 1; beat 3, dyad changed to triad with added f in *Emend* 1. Mm. 152 and 153, **GPR** directives are crossed out in *Emend* 1. M. 155, **GPR** is written above staff 2, note 2 in *Emend* 1.)

II. Choral

The Choral commences in a most arresting manner. Visually, one is struck by a page of six-part writing; on closer examination, however, the theme is seen to be harmonized in four-part chorale style, enhanced by double pedal—the upper voice duplicates the soprano line and the lower voice provides a firm bass. Aurally, this broad, spacious style of writing, intensified by a registration of sub, unison, and octave stops, yields a rich timbral spectrum that spreads out over almost seven octaves in some measures (e.g., m. 19, beat 3). After the opening section, which states the chorale twice, contrasting minor-mode material in an agitated triple meter is introduced. Returns of the chorale and the contrasting material, a free combination of the two, and finally a complete variation and coda on the chorale conclude the formal structure. Widor's potency in fashioning musical development is once again in evidence; one cannot help but admire the ingenuity with which he handles his material. In fact, when heard in the context of the whole symphony, the Choral emerges as a clear exposition of what might be considered the work's *Urmotif*. The opening melodic phrase appears in every movement, though sometimes in rhythmic or melodic mutation. The Choral was never revised. Edition *E* is the principal source.

CRITICAL NOTES

M. 104, staff 2, beat 3, lower voice (e[-sharp]), *Riem* 7 has a natural with a question mark; since the natural is clearly marked in beat 4, the editor takes the source reading at face value. M. 106, staff 1, beat 4, note 8, the editorial natural conforms to *Riem* 7. M. 110, staff 2, beat 4 has eighth rest—an error. M. 118, the cre-

scendo hairpin is located in the same metrical position, but below staff 2, and a second, short crescendo hairpin is located between staves 1 and 2, on beat 4, in all editions; dynamic hairpins for the unexpressive **G** are problematic; the editor suggests coupling the Récit Flûtes 8', 4' (as in m. 73), and beginning with the expression box closed on beat 3. A slight *allargando* may also be appropriate here, following Widor's maxim that "*allargando* and *crescendo* are almost synonymous in organ music."*

III

By 1887 Widor had published well over fifty *mélodies*; his proficiency with the French art song is evidenced by the pervading lyrical quality in this music. The lilting rhythms and airy texture bring the first breath of light-heartedness to the symphony. At the same time, counterpoint is never far away in Widor's art. Here even the simple accompanying parts lend more than mere harmonic support; they often vie for the listener's attention as countermelodies in a free, sometimes triolike texture that is emphasized by the colorful registration. The ternary form of the piece is clear, yet within each section Widor resourcefully avoids any pallid restatement of the material. There are three very similar versions: *B*, *B'/C*, and *C'/D/E*. Reports on the variant readings of versions *B* and *B'/C* follow the critical notes for version *C'/D/E* below. For the final version, edition *E* is the principal source.

This movement suffers from a common problem that plagues many Hamelle pressings: staccato dots and other fine details fade in and out of different editions, edition *E* usually being the most problematic. Details that obviously faded from edition *E* have been tacitly reinstated. Other apparent, unintentional irregularities in the staccato and tenuto marks between parallel measures have been tacitly regularized.

The ornament signs in mm. 13, 23, 60, 181, and 191 are given as ∿ in editions *B* and *B'*; thereafter, the sign in m. 23 only is given ⁓. The symphonies have the latter sign almost exclusively elsewhere, even on very short notes (see, for example, Symphonie VI: first movement, m. 109; second movement, m. 91; fourth movement, mm. 59, 76); thus there are strong reasons to suppose that the short sign does not indicate fewer percussions. The choice of signs probably resulted from the engraver's decision rather than authorial direction. Why the short sign in m. 23 was replaced is an enigma. (All the short signs in Symphonie IV, first movement, were replaced by long signs in edition *C'*.) In any case, whether written short or long, the ornament should be performed main note, upper auxiliary, main note.

CRITICAL NOTES

M. 13, staff 1, note 1 has ornament (∿) in editions *B* through *D*—the editor believes the ornament simply

---

*See Charles-Marie Widor, preface to *Jean-Sébastien Bach: Oeuvres complètes pour orgue*, 1 (New York: G. Schirmer, 1914), vi.

faded from available pressings of edition *E*; it appears in *Emend* 2 with no indication for deletion and remains in edition *E* in analogous m. 181 (the situation in analogous m. 60 is more complicated; see report below); note 1 has no staccato dot in any edition—edition follows analogous m. 181; even if the performer elects to omit the ornament on note 1, the staccato should certainly be retained. M. 15, staff 3, note 1 has no dot—this is another instance of fading due to aging plates. Mm. 23–24, staff 2, upper voice, editorial extension of the slur follows the slurring of staff 1 and that of similar mm. 70–71.

M. 58, staff 1, notes 2 and 3 are staccato in all editions—edition follows analogous mm. 11 and 179; the engraver likely placed the staccato dots erroneously in m. 58 instead of m. 59, staff 1, notes 1 and 2, which are not staccato in any edition and yet should be to conform to analogous mm. 12 and 180. M. 59, staff 1, editorial slur follows analogous mm. 12 and 180. M. 60, staff 1, note 1 has no ornament—the ornament is also faded in *C'*, and it is nearly faded in *D*, illustrating the serious and capricious nature of the printing flaws from edition to edition; the ornament does appear in *Emend* 2 with no indication for deletion; see also report for m. 13. Mm. 69–71, staff 2 differs slightly from analogous mm. 22–24 and 190–92 in that it retains the original *B* reading; though the question of oversight might be raised, Widor probably left this passage as a variant—like many others in this movement—to avoid punctilious repetition. M. 70, staff 1, note 1, the ornament is given as ∿ in all editions—edition conforms to the longer form generally effected in *C*. Mm. 72–74, staff 1, editorial slur follows analogous mm. 25–27. M. 88, staff 1, lower voice is altered to quarter note, eighth rest in *Riem* 7. M. 96, the Récit Trompette is certainly meant to be added to the Clarinette, as in m. 36—the Clarinette (Cromorne at Saint-Sulpice) is located on the wind chest with the Fonds, the Trompette with the Jeux de combinaison; with the Trompette drawn in preparation, activating the Récit Jeux de combinaison (Anches) pedal would add it to the Clarinette.*

M. 129, staff 2, beat 2, note 1 has no downstem in any edition—edition follows analogous m. 147. M. 133, staff 1, upper voice, editorial tie follows analogous m. 123. M. 143, staff 1 has whole rest and two eighth rests—an error. M. 161, staff 2, the grace notes are placed in m. 160 in all editions—edition follows Widor's usual practice of placing grace notes after the barline, though they are played before the beat. M. 173, "Tempo I" is indicated in all editions—this is misleading in that the return should be to Allegretto, not Andante. M. 190, staff 2, upper voice, editorial slur follows analogous m. 22. M. 191, staff 1, note 1, the ornament is given as (∿) in all editions—edition conforms to longer form generally effected in *C*; staff 2, upper voice, editorial extension of the slur follows the slurring of staff 1 and that of similar m. 70. M. 192, staff 2, upper voice, editorial extension of the slur follows the slurring of staff 1 and that of similar m. 71. Mm. 193–95, staff 1, editorial slur follows analogous mm. 25–27. M. 195, staff 2, the notes are stemmed together in all editions—separate stemming follows analogous m. 74.

M. 203, staff 1, upper voice, note 3, editorial tie to m. 204, note 1, follows analogous m. 82. M. 206, staff 1, upper voice, note has no dot in any edition—an error. M. 209, staff 1, lower voice, see report for analogous m. 88. M. 225, see report for analogous m. 96. M. 232–33, staff 1, the slur would break between these measures to follow the phrasing in analogous mm. 43–44 and 103–4—this may be Widor's intention here, too: m. 232 is located at the end of a system in the source, and the engraver may have erroneously continued the slur too far and then picked it up again in the following system. M. 234, staff 2, upper voice, editorial tie follows analogous m. 105.

Version *B'/C* differs from version *C'/D/E* as follows. The registration for the Pédale is "Basses de 8 et de 16"; mm. 113, 170, and 214, staff 3 has no registration directives (adding, removing, and adding 16' pitch). Mm. 110, 111, 239, and 240, staff 3, note 2 is staccato f[-sharp]. M. 245, staff 3 has slur to m. 248, lower voice.

Edition *B* differs from version *B'/C* as follows. M. 3, staff 2, lower voice, note 1 has no staccato, note 2 is dotted half note tied into m. 4. M. 4, staff 2, lower voice is tied c[-sharp] half note tied to c[-sharp] dotted quarter note, eighth rest. Mm. 22–24 (and analogous mm. 190–92), staff 2 has no lower voice, and note 1 (g'[-sharp]) of m. 22 (and m. 190) has c'[-sharp] grace note (see mm. 69–71 of *E*, where the *B* reading was retained).

IV

Of all the movements in the organ symphonies, this one stands out as the most étudelike, especially in its original version. A friend and ardent admirer of Liszt, Widor may have found the model for this *tour de force* in the sixth of Liszt's *Études d'exécution transcendente* ("Vision") for piano. The main theme, in long notes, rides over an accompaniment altogether extraordinary for the organ, a flurry of arpeggiated figuration (with beat groups containing variously from four to seven notes) that rises and falls like great waves. The technique, clearly pianistic, requires one to maintain a legato melody in the upper voice against a turbulent flow of notes below.

The principal theme is based on the opening phrase of the Choral movement (see Appendix 2, m. 12, staff 1, upper voice; the original break in the melodic line [in beat 3] clearly shows this relationship). Stated in the tonic minor, this placid melody is at first extended (as it moves to the mediant), then fragmented and transformed (beginning at m. 21), then brought back in its nascent form (at m. 44), and finally dissolved into a new

---

*For a description of technical aspects of the Saint-Sulpice organ together with its specification, see Performance Guidelines in the Preface to this edition (vol. 11, Symphonie I, xxi).

section (beginning at m. 67, beat 3). A more animated second theme is heard twice before the opening material returns briefly in a new key (m. 85); but the original accompaniment soon gives way to a new pattern (m. 93)—related to the accompaniment of the second theme—that takes on a life of its own as the movement concludes, still intoning the main theme.

The movement exists in four versions: B/B', C, C'/D, and E. Until measure 101, version B/B' is roughly analogous to the later versions (there are some additional measures and the arpeggiated figurations are often different); but the following section, the return of the second theme, and the free recapitulation of the main theme with its original style of accompaniment are different. Version B/B' is given as Appendix 2. In revising the movement for edition C, Widor shortened it by some forty-four measures. Versions C, C'/D, and E are quite similar. The variant section of edition C is given as Appendix 3, and reports on the variants in version C'/D follow the critical notes below. For the final version, edition E is the principal source.

Riem 7 contains a few emendations (all in ink except as noted) that appear to be in Widor's hand, as follows. M. 25, staff 2, beat 1 is sixteenth rest, f-sharp, B, f[-sharp], a, b sixteenth notes. M. 26, staff 2, beat 3 is f[-sharp], a, d-sharp, a, B, a sixteenth notes. M. 27, staff 2, beat 1, note 2 is B, and beat 3, note 3 is d (both in pencil). M. 36, see Critical Notes. M. 49, staves 1 and 2, the figuration in beat 1 is B, e, g-sharp, b sixteenth notes; beat 2 is d', e', g'[-sharp], e', d', b sixteenth notes; beat 3 is e, g[-sharp], b, d' sixteenth notes. M. 50, staff 2 has lower voice e half note tied to e eighth note, eighth rest. M. 51, staves 1 and 2, the figuration in beat 1 is g-sharp, a, c', e' sixteenth notes; beat 2 is g'[-sharp], a', b', a' sixteenth notes. Mm. 69 and 77, see Critical Notes. M. 81, staff 2 is g' quarter note, f'-sharp half note.

CRITICAL NOTES

M. 24, staff 1, upper voice, beat 3, note has no eighth flag in C, C'/D, and E—an error. M. 36, staff 1, beat 2, lower voice, the cautionary sharp for grace note g' follows *Riem* 7. M. 55, staff 3, editorial directive conforms to manual directives in m. 56, and follows directive in analogous m. 63 in B/B'—see Appendix 2. M. 60, staff 1, beat 1, note has no downstem in any edition—edition follows similar m. 64. M. 65 and 67, staff 2, upper voice, beat 1 is quarter note in C, C'/D, and E—editorial shortening of the note conforms to m. 66 and the analogous measures in B/B', and it allows repetition of the note later in the beat. M. 68, staff 2, slur begins on note 1 in C, C'/D, and E, even though a slur begins on beat 3 in the previous measure (the last measure on the page in the source)—the engraver neglected to continue the slur onto the new page; the slurring is correct when the theme repeats, beginning in m. 75. Mm. 69 and 77, staff 1, beat 3, the cautionary sharp for d' follows *Riem* 7, where it is inserted in both measures in ink. M. 79, staff 2, beat 3, there is no caesura in some prints of E—this is another instance of fading due to aging plates. M. 80, staff 2, slur is shown to be continued from the previous measure (the last measure on the page in the source) in C, C'/D, and E, even though the slur clearly ends on beat 3 in m. 79 (the slurring is correct at similar m. 72). M. 82, *animato* is located over note 2. M. 84, staff 3, editorial directive conforms to manual directives in mm. 84 and 85, and follows directive in analogous m. 93 in B/B'—see Appendix 2. Mm. 97 and 98, staff 3, the editorial directives seem appropriate to prepare the Pédale to take the staff-2, lower-voice part, and to balance the manual **GPR**; the directives follow the analogous passage (m. 107) in B/B'—see Appendix 2.

Mm. 108–12, staff 1, editorial continuation of the slur to the end of the main theme follows m. 107 (the last measure of a system in the source) which shows that the slur was to continue. M. 114, staff 3, note 1 is dotted (as if in $\frac{9}{8}$)—an error. M. 115, staff 3, beat 3 has quarter rest, eighth rest (as if in $\frac{9}{8}$)—an error. M. 116, staff 1, beat 1, upper voice, note is dotted—an error; lower voice, note 1 is c' in E—this is clearly an engraver's error, made when the passage was reengraved; edition follows C'/D and conforms to tied a dotted half note from m. 115; staff 1, beat 2, lower voice, note is dotted (as if in $\frac{9}{8}$)—an error; staff 2, note 1 is dotted (as if in $\frac{9}{8}$)—an error; staff 3, beats 2 and 3 have quarter rest, eighth rest (as if in $\frac{9}{8}$)—errors. Mm. 123–24, staff 1, editorial continuation of the slur follows m. 122 (the last measure of a system in the source), which shows that the slur was to continue. M. 129, staff 3, half rest has no dot—an error. M. 131, staff 1, editorial continuation of the slurs follows m. 130 (the last measure of a system in the source), which shows that the slurs were to continue. Mm. 139–44, staff 1 is in alto clef.

Version C'/D differs from edition E as follows. M. 112, staff 1, beat 3 has no **R**. M. 114, staff 3, notes 2 and 3 are quarter notes. M. 115, staff 3, note 1 is quarter note, note 2 is half note. M. 116, staff 1, upper voice, beat 3, note 2 has **R**; lower voice is on staff 2, and note 5 (tied g[-sharp]) is eighth note; staff 3 is E half note tied to E eighth note, eighth rest. M. 126, staff 3, beat 2 is f-sharp eighth note, F-sharp quarter note; beat 3 is F-natural dotted quarter note. M. 127, staff 3, beat 1 is staccato F eighth note and two eighth rests. Mm. 128 and 129, staff 3, note 1 is C staccato eighth note.

V

A certain spiritual serenity reigns in this slow movement, where spaciousness, luscious harmonies, and delicate rhythmic configurations contribute to the rarefied atmosphere. Again the symphony's *Urmotif* can be clearly traced (see especially mm. 24–27).

The movement exists in four versions: B, B', C, and C'/D/E. Editions B and B' are nearly identical—a half dozen measures were modified for B'. Widor tended to avoid coloristic effects, but in these early editions the Voix humaine—so rarely heard in the symphonies—colors alternating passages with its uniquely ethereal timbre. Edition *B'* displays such fine quality and differs so extensively from the final version that it warrants performance in its own right. Appendix 4 gives editions *B* and *B'*—the latter as an *ossia* in the variant measures. A few refinements separate edition *C* and version *C'/D/E*; the variant measures of edition *C* are given as Appendix 5. For the final version, edition *E* is the principal source.

Riem 7 shows two small emendations that Widor likely suggested. M. 37, see Critical Notes. M. 39, staff 2, upper voice, note 1 is tied b, and note 2 is b-sharp. M. 67, staff 2, upper voice is a dotted eighth note, b[-natural] sixteenth note, a quarter note.

CRITICAL NOTES

M. 1, staff 3, the absence of **R** in the directive likely stems from *B* and *B'*, where **R** is Voix humaine (the manual directive is also **GP** in those editions). M. 13, staves 1 and 2, the absence of **R** in the directive is certainly an oversight—the directive was not corrected for editions after *B'*—edition follows mm. 1 and 23. M. 21, staff 1, slur is shown as coming from m. 20 (located at the bottom of the previous page in the source), but m. 20 has no slur. M. 22, staff 1, beat 2, upper voice, note is dotted—an error. M. 26, staff 1, lower voice, editorial tie follows analogous m. 25 in *B* and *B'*—the tie was apparently omitted in error when the passage was reengraved. M. 29, staff 1, middle voice, editorial tie to m. 30, note 1, follows analogous mm. 25–26. M. 37, staves 1 and 2, lower voices, note 1, editorial naturals follow *Riem* 7. M. 66, staff 2, lower voice, note 1 has no dot—an error.

VI. Finale

The atmosphere of the first movement is intensified in the Finale; here is epoch-making organ music, new and thrilling—even hair-raising—in its conception. Against stark open fifths, the modally oriented main theme (related to the symphony's *Urmotif*) is first intoned like a medieval plainchant, and it receives a variety of treatments throughout the free, fantasielike movement. The seemingly insignificant descending pedal part in measures 18–20 soon becomes a primary element, and after measure 209 it transforms into a figuration recalling the cascading accompaniment in Wagner's *Tannhäuser* overture.

There are three versions of the movement: *B/B'*, *C*, and *C'/D/E*. They are nearly identical until measure 236; the variant reading of the final seventy-one measures of version *B/B'* appears as Appendix 6; reports on the variant readings of edition *C* follow the critical notes for version *C'/D/E* below. For the final version, edition *E* is the principal source.

CRITICAL NOTES

Mm. 14 and 15, staves 1 and 2 have caesuras before beat 3 in *Schw* 7–8. M. 18, staves 1 and 2, beat 1 through m. 21, beat 1, have slurs in *Schw* 7–8. Mm. 54, 55, 58, and 59, staff 1, beat 1, all three notes are stemmed together—edition follows separate stemming of mm. 56, 57, and 60–69, which represent the majority voicing of the passage; note also, in mm. 55 and 59, beats 2 and 3, how the quarter rests imply two voices (just as they do in double-stemmed mm. 56 and 60). M. 98, staff 1, beat 1, notes are stemmed together. M. 109, staves 1 and 2, there is no manual directive in any edition—an error; edition follows analogous m. 107; **GPR** has been written into *Riem* 7. Mm. 111–14 and 119–22, staff 1, mm. 115–18 and 123, staff 2, beat 3, lower note is staccato only in all editions—the tenuto dashes added here follow *Emend* 1 and *Riem* 7. M. 123, staff 1, note 4, the cautionary double-flat follows *Riem* 7. M. 125, staff 2, beat 3, lower note, the editorial natural follows *Riem* 7. M. 137, staff 1, beat 3 is slurred to m. 138, beat 1—edition follows analogous m. 149 (*Riem* 7 has a caesura in place of the slur); staff 3, beat 3 has no quarter rest in any edition—an error.

M. 155, staff 1, beat 1, all notes are stemmed down—upstem follows analogous m. 143. M. 156, staves 1 and 2, beat 1, c″-flat and c‴-flat have no stems in *C'*, *D*, and *E*—this is another instance of fading due to aging plates. M. 182, staff 3, beat 3 is G eighth note, eighth rest in all editions—this is certainly an engraver's error as it breaks the pattern of the passage; *Riem* 7 has a slur to m. 183, beat 1, inserted. Mm. 197–200, staff 2, lower voice, all staccato dots are crossed out in *Riem* 7.

M. 209, staff 2, note 4, editorial sharp follows analogous m. 211 and *Riem* 7. M. 235, staff 1, note 8, coming at the end of a system, has purposeless tie that should have been deleted after *B'*, when the following measure was revised. M. 291, staff 2 apparently remains **GPR**; if the balance is poor, however, the performer could move to **PR** or **R** until m. 303, beat 1 (*Riem* 7 indicates the return to **G[PR]** there).

M. 304, staff 1, upper voice, note 1 is dotted—an error; the eighth rest in the second half of beat 2 is for the middle voice; a quarter rest on beat 3 is omitted to avoid congestion. M. 322, staff 1, beat 2, the natural for g″ is misplaced on the e″ line—an error.

Edition *C* differs from version *C'/D/E* as follows. Mm. 233 and 236 have no repeat bars. M. 287, staff 3 is E dotted half note (no tie to m. 288). Mm. 298–311, see plate 2.

Appendix 1

I. Editions B and B', mm. 160–68. Edition *B'* variant appears as an *ossia*. *Emend-1 sketch, mm. 161–68*, is given synoptically.

To perform edition *B* or *B'* complete, play measures 1–159 of edition *E*, noting the variants reported below; then this Appendix; then measures 169–76 of edition *E*.

Mm. 26, 28, 30, and 31, staff 1, beat 3 is staccato eighth chord, staccato sixteenth chord, thirty-second rest, staccato thirty-second chord. M. 34, in edition *B* only, staff 1, beat 1, chord has e‴ instead of e″; staff 2, beat 1, chord has e″ instead of e′. M. 79, staff 3, note 2, through m. 84, note 1, all notes are staccato. M. 146, staff 2, beat 3 has **G** and m. 147, staff 1, beat 2 has **G**—

these manual directives signify **G** solo. On most organs the Positif and Récit must be uncoupled from the Grand-orgue at this point; at Saint-Sulpice, however, one needs only to move from the Grand-choeur (**GPR**) to the Grand-orgue (**G**). The problem is at the return to **GPR** in m. 152; Widor created an impossibility on most organs by indicating **GPR** for the right hand while keeping the left hand **G**. Another solution will have to be sought; perhaps returning to **GPR** at m. 155, note 2 (as suggested in *Emend* 1) is best.   M. 166, staves 1 and 2, beat 2 has no *p* in edition *B'*.

Appendix 2

IV. Version B/B'. Edition *B'* is the principal source. M. 36, staff 1, beat 2, lower voice, the cautionary sharp for grace note g' follows *Riem* 7.   M. 72, staff 3, the directive indicates no coupler—an error.   Mm. 77 and 85, staff 1, beat 3, the cautionary sharp for d' follows *Riem* 7, where it is inserted in both measures in ink.   M. 116, staff 1, lower voice, beat 2 has eighth rest—an error.   M. 122, staff 1, middle voice, note has no dot—an error.   M. 126 and 127, staff 1, beat 2, lower-voice dyad is half notes—an error.   Mm. 129–31, staff 1, beat 1, note 1 is also stemmed down as dotted eighth note tied to beat 2, and note 2 is stemmed down as eighth note (slurred in m. 129 and tied in mm. 130 and 131) to beat 2—while this notation is correct, it is uncharacteristic of Widor's orthography in this situation (e.g., see mm. 76, 77, 81, etc.)—edition follows the majority practice.

Appendix 3

IV. Edition C, mm. 108–32. To perform this edition complete, play mm. 1–107 of edition *E*, noting the variants reported below; then this Appendix; then mm. 133–44 of edition *E*.

M. 42, staff 2, beat 1 has no f dotted eighth note.   M. 74, staff 3 has whole rest.   M. 75, staff 3 has eighth rest, A, D, d, A, a staccato eighth notes.   M. 107, staff 1, beat 1, lower voice is eighth rest, e', c' eighth notes.   M. 113, staff 2, note 2 has no sixteenth flag—an error.

Appendix 4

V. Editions B and B'. Edition *B'* variants appear as *ossia*s.   M. 17, staff 1, upper voice, slur extends to d"[-sharp]—an error.   M. 26, staff 1, beat 1, upper voice, note 2 has no downstem—edition follows m. 22 and majority voicing of the passage.   M. 35, staff 1, manual directive and slur in *B'* follow *Emend* 1—see following report.   M. 36, staff 1, upper voice, note 1 has **G** and the slur begins in *B'*.   M. 40, staff 2, notes 1 and 2, fermatas in *B'* follow *Emend* 1.   M. 45, staff 2, note 2 is dotted—an error.

Appendix 5

V. Edition C, mm. 38–50. To perform this edition complete, play mm. 1–37 of version *C'/D/E*, noting the variants reported below; then this Appendix; then mm. 51–69 of version *C'/D/E*, again noting the variants reported below.

M. 31, staff 1, directive reads "(**R** Fonds 4, 8, 16)."   M. 35, staff 2, beat 2 has no **R** directive—an error.   M. 37, staves 1 and 2, beat 1 has no *cresc.*; beat 2, notes 3–5 have crescendo hairpin, note 6 has decrescendo hairpin.   M. 45, staff 1, lower voice, note 9, editorial natural follows *C'/D/E*.   M. 48, staff 3, note has tie and slur to m. 49—the tie is an error.

M. 55, staves 1 and 2, beat 2 has no *ff*—an error.   M. 64, staff 2, beat 2, note is f-double-sharp eighth note.   M. 65, staff 2, upper voice is g[-sharp] eighth note, a dotted quarter note tied to m. 66.   M. 66, staff 1, upper voice, note 6 has no dot—an error.   M. 67, staves 1 and 2 have no decrescendo hairpin—an error.   M. 68, staves 1 and 2, beat 2 has short crescendo and decrescendo hairpins centered under d'-double-sharp.   M. 69, staves 1 and 2 have no crescendo and decrescendo hairpins.

Appendix 6

VI. Finale. Version B/B', mm. 235–305. To perform this version complete, play mm. 1–234 of version *C'/D/E*, noting the variants reported below; then this Appendix. Edition *B'* is the principal source.

M. 89, staff 3, beat 1 is c staccato quarter note.   M. 90, staff 3 is c staccato quarter note, c' half note.   M. 91, staff 3, beat 1 is c staccato eighth note, c' staccato eighth note.   M. 162, staff 2, beat 1 is c, d eighth notes; beat 2 is e[-flat] quarter note.   M. 164, staff 3, directive is "**Péd. GPR**."   M. 165, staff 2 is tied g dotted half note; staff 3 has no dynamic mark.   M. 197–200, staff 2, lower voice has no staccato dots.   M. 199, staff 1, upper voice is tied b" dotted half note tied to next measure; staff 2, upper voice is tied b' half note, e" quarter note.   M. 200, staff 1, upper voice is tied b" dotted half note.   M. 233 has no repeat barline.   M. 286, staff 2, beat 3, lower voice, there is no eighth rest on second half of beat—an error.

Widor's *Avant-propos*

Although it may not be customary to place a preface at the front of musical editions, I believe it is necessary to put one here in order to explain the character, the style, the procedures of registration, and the sign conventions of these eight symphonies.

Old instruments had almost no reed stops: two colors, white and black, foundation stops and mixture stops—that was their entire palette; moreover, each transition between this white and this black was abrupt and rough; the means of graduating the body of sound did not exist. Consequently, Bach and his contemporaries deemed it pointless to indicate registrations for their works—the mixture stops traditionally remaining appropriate to rapid movements, and the foundation stops to pieces of a more solemn pace.

The invention of the "swell box" dates back to just before the end of the eighteenth century. In a work published in 1772, the Dutchman Hess de Gouda expresses the admiration he felt upon hearing Handel, in London, coming to grips with the new device; some time later, in 1780, Abbé Vogler recommends the use of the "box" in the German manufacture of instruments. The idea gained ground, but without great artistic effect—for in spite of the most perspicacious efforts,* they did not succeed in going beyond the limits of a thirty-key manual and an insignificant number of registers.

It was necessary to wait until 1839 for the solution to the problem.

The honor for it redounds to French industry and the glory to Mr. A. Cavaillé-Coll. It is he who conceived the diverse wind pressures, the divided windchests, the pedal systems and the combination registers, he who applied for the first time Barker's pneumatic motors, created the family of harmonic stops, reformed and perfected the mechanics to such a point that each pipe—low or high, loud or soft—instantly obeys the touch of the finger, the keys becoming as light as those of a piano—the resistances being suppressed, rendering the combination of [all] the forces of the instrument practical. From this result: the possibility of confining an entire division in a sonorous prison—opened or closed at will—the freedom of mixing timbres, the means of intensifying them or gradually tempering them, the freedom of tempos, the sureness of attacks, the balance of contrasts, and, finally, a whole blossoming of wonderful colors—a rich palette of the most diverse shades: harmonic flutes, gambas, bassoons, English horns, trumpets, celestes, flue stops and reed stops of a quality and variety unknown before.

The modern organ is essentially symphonic. The new instrument requires a new language, an ideal other than scholastic polyphony. It is no longer the Bach of the fugue whom we invoke but the heartrending melodist, the preeminently expressive master of the Preludes, the Magnificat, the B-minor Mass, the cantatas, and the *St. Matthew Passion.*

But this "expressiveness" of the new instrument can only be subjective; it arises from mechanical means and cannot have spontaneity. While the stringed and wind instruments of the orchestra, the piano, and voices reign only by naturalness of accent and unexpectedness of attack, the organ, clothed in its primordial majesty, speaks as a philosopher: alone among all, it can put forth the same volume of sound indefinitely and thus inspire the religious idea of the infinite. Surprises and accents are not natural to it; they are lent to it, they are accents by adoption. It is clear that their use requires tact and discernment. It is also clear to what extent the organ symphony differs from the orchestral symphony. No confusion is to be feared. One will never write indiscriminately for the orchestra or for the organ, but henceforth one will have to exercise the same care with the combination of timbres in an organ composition as in an orchestral work.

Rhythm itself must come under the influence of modern trends: it must lend itself to a sort of elasticity of the measure, all the while preserving its rights. It must allow the musical phrase to punctuate its paragraphs and breathe when necessary, provided that it hold [the phrase] by the bit and that [the phrase] march to its step. Without rhythm, without this constant manifestation of the will returning periodically to the strong beat, the performer will not be listened to. How often the composer hesitates and abstains at the moment of writing on his score the *poco ritenuto* that he has in his thought! He does not dare, from fear that the exaggeration of the performer may weaken or break the flow of the piece. The indication is left out. We do not have the graphic means for emphasizing the end of a period, or reinforcing a chord by a type of pause of unnoticeable duration. Isn't it a great shame, especially since the organ is an instrument that draws all of its effect from time values?

As to terminology, the system indicating the disposition of timbres—usage having established nothing as yet—it seemed practical to me to note the manual and pedal registration at the head of each piece; to apportion by tone colors, rather than an exact nomenclature of stops, the intensity of the sonorities of the same family; to designate the manuals by their abbreviations (two or

---

*Experiments of Sébastien Erard: Organ constructed in 1826 for the chapel of the Legion of Honor at St.-Denis—Exposition at the Louvre in 1827.

more initials juxtaposed signifying the coupling of two or more manuals); to assume the reed stops always prepared; and finally to reserve fff for the full power of the organ, without having to mention the introduction of the ventil (Anches) pedals. In the combination **GR** [Grand-orgue, Récit], the crescendo applies only to the Récit, unless this crescendo leads to the fff, in which case all the forces of the instrument must enter little by little in order, flues and reeds.

It is unnecessary, I believe, to implore the same precision, the same coordination of the feet and hands in leaving a keyboard as in attacking it, and to protest against all carrying-over of the pedal after the time, an old-fashioned custom that has happily almost disappeared.

With the consummate musicians of today, the insufficiencies and shortcomings in musical notation become less worrisome; the composer is more certain of seeing his intentions understood and his implications perceived. Between him and the performer is a steadfast collaboration, which the growing number of virtuosos will render more intimate and fruitful every day.

Ch. M. W.

Plate 1. Symphonie VII: I, copy *Emend* 2, page 3, systems 2–4, comprising measures 20–34. The *Emend*-2 copy of Symphonie VII is edition *D* (for further discussion, see Sources, "Autograph Revisions" in the Preface to this edition, vol. 11, Symphonie I, xv–xvii). The present edition follows the emendations made in the right-hand margin for measures 26 and 28, and those made at the bottom of the page for measures 30 and 31; the revised rhythm and articulation are clearly marked there. Widor apparently began marking the emendation on the music itself by adding sixteenth flags to the eighth-note chords in mm. 26, 28 and 30, but deferred to marginal sketches for maximum clarity of intent.

Courtesy Bibliothèque nationale, Paris

Plate 2. Symphonie VII: VI. Finale, copy *Schw* 7–8, page 282, systems 3–4, comprising measures 298–311. Although this passage was revised further for edition *C'*, Widor's hand-written emendations here reveal a fascinating point. In measures 309–10, by employing double pedal, Widor piles as many notes into the first-inversion C-major chord as the feet and hands can manage. Big chords, even at cadences, are sometimes more leanly written by omitting one or more chord members that might appear to overload or clog the sound (for example, see the last F-major chord at the end of Symphonie V: V. Toccata). In practice, however, one might wonder whether or not Widor actually resisted the temptation to fill in such chords to the fullest degree, especially on a less powerful organ.

      Courtesy Maison Schweitzer, Gunsbach, France

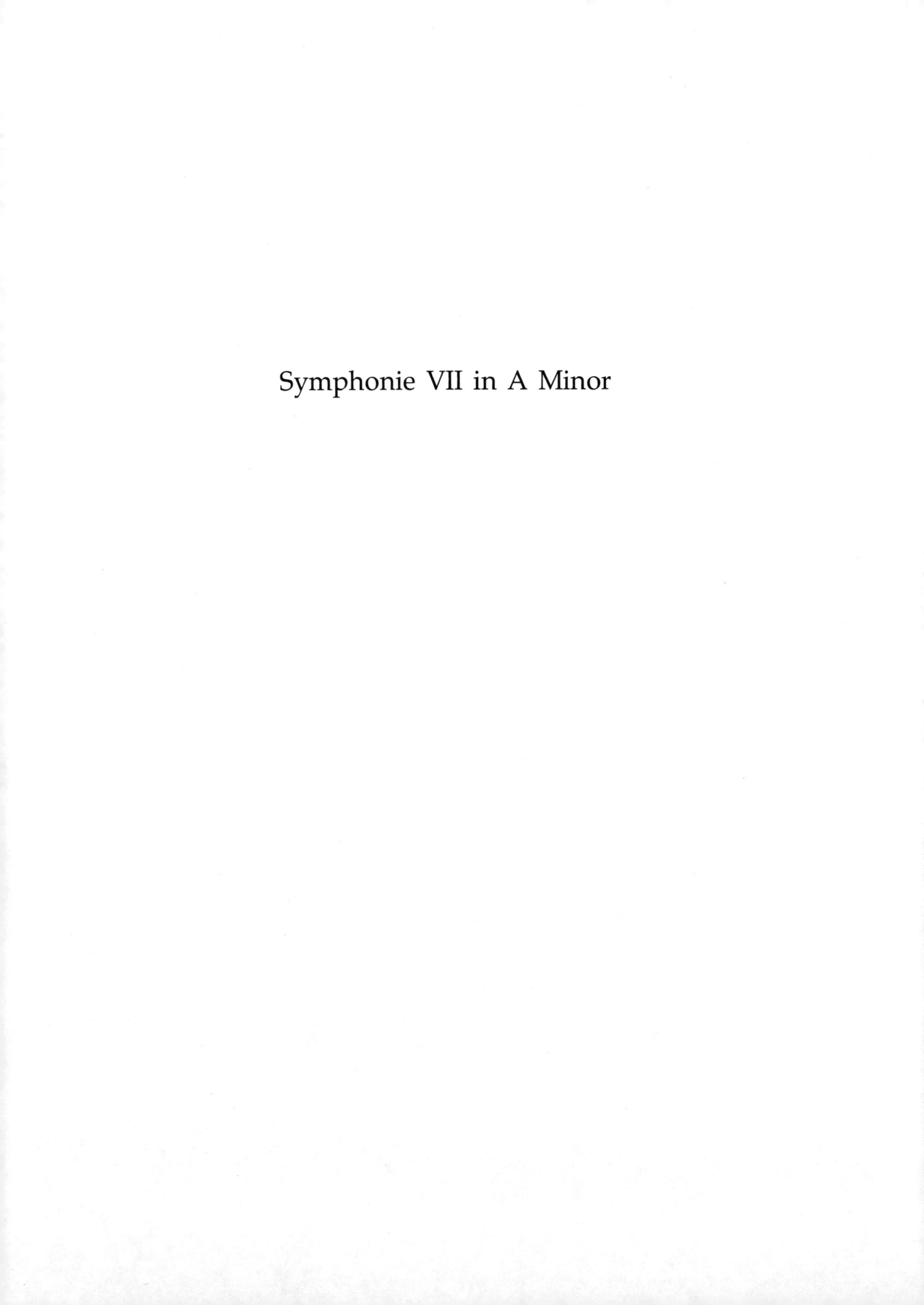

Symphonie VII in A Minor

Grand orgue:
Positif: Fonds et Anches 16', 8', 4'
Récit:
Pédale: Fonds et Anches [32',]16', 8', 4'

I

Moderato (♩ = 88)

[GPR] *fff*

fff

[Péd. GPR]

II. Choral

Grand orgue: Fonds 16', 8'
Positif: [Gambe 8',] Voix céleste
Récit: Flûtes 8', 4'
Pédale: Basse 16'

Andante (♩ = 52)

G Fonds 8'
rit.
(R Flûte 8')
G
Andantino agitato (♩. = 69)
(G meno f)
P pp
poco cresc.
mf
Péd. PR
Péd. GPR

G
G
PR
Péd. tacet.
R Flûte 8'
Andante
8va
R pp
Péd. R (Flûte 8' de Récit seule)
(8va)
Andantino agitato
(R Flûtes 8', 4')
P pp
(Péd. Basses 16', 8')

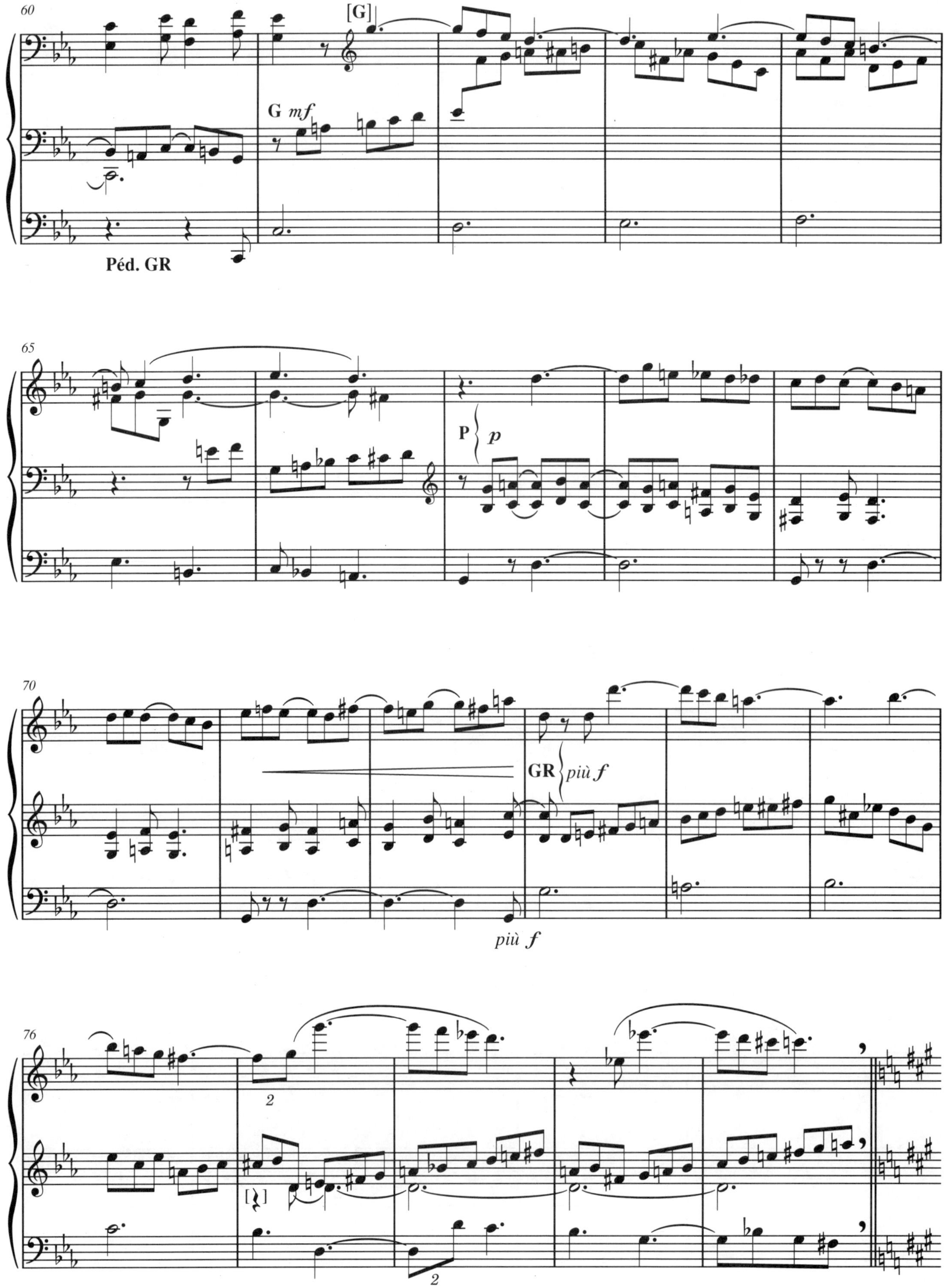
60
[G]
G mf
Péd. GR
65
P
p
70
GR
più f
più f
76

81
poco allargando
(G Fonds 16', 8', 4')
P f
f
a tempo
GR f
86
91
poco rit.
a tempo
96
R

Tempo I
101
a piacere
(G Fonds 8')
pp
p
[]
p
104
riten.
a tempo
[]
G
[6]
[6]
f
106
[6]
3
108
[6]
R

19

20

*See Critical Notes.

Grand orgue: Flûte 8'
Positif: Flûte 8'
Récit: Clarinette [8']
Pédale: Basses 8'

III

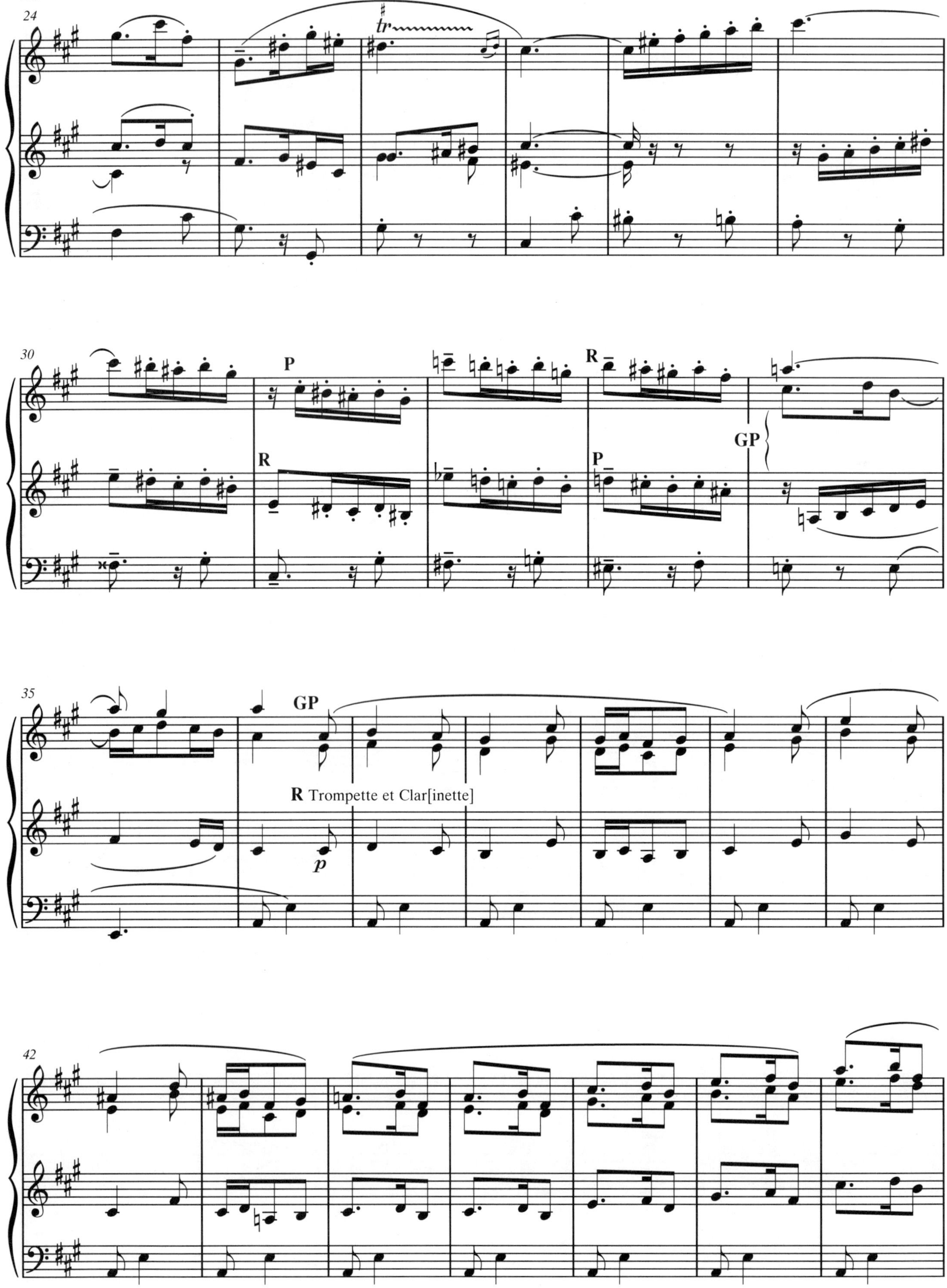
24
tr
30
P
R
GP
P
R
35
GP
R Trompette et Clar[inette]
p
42

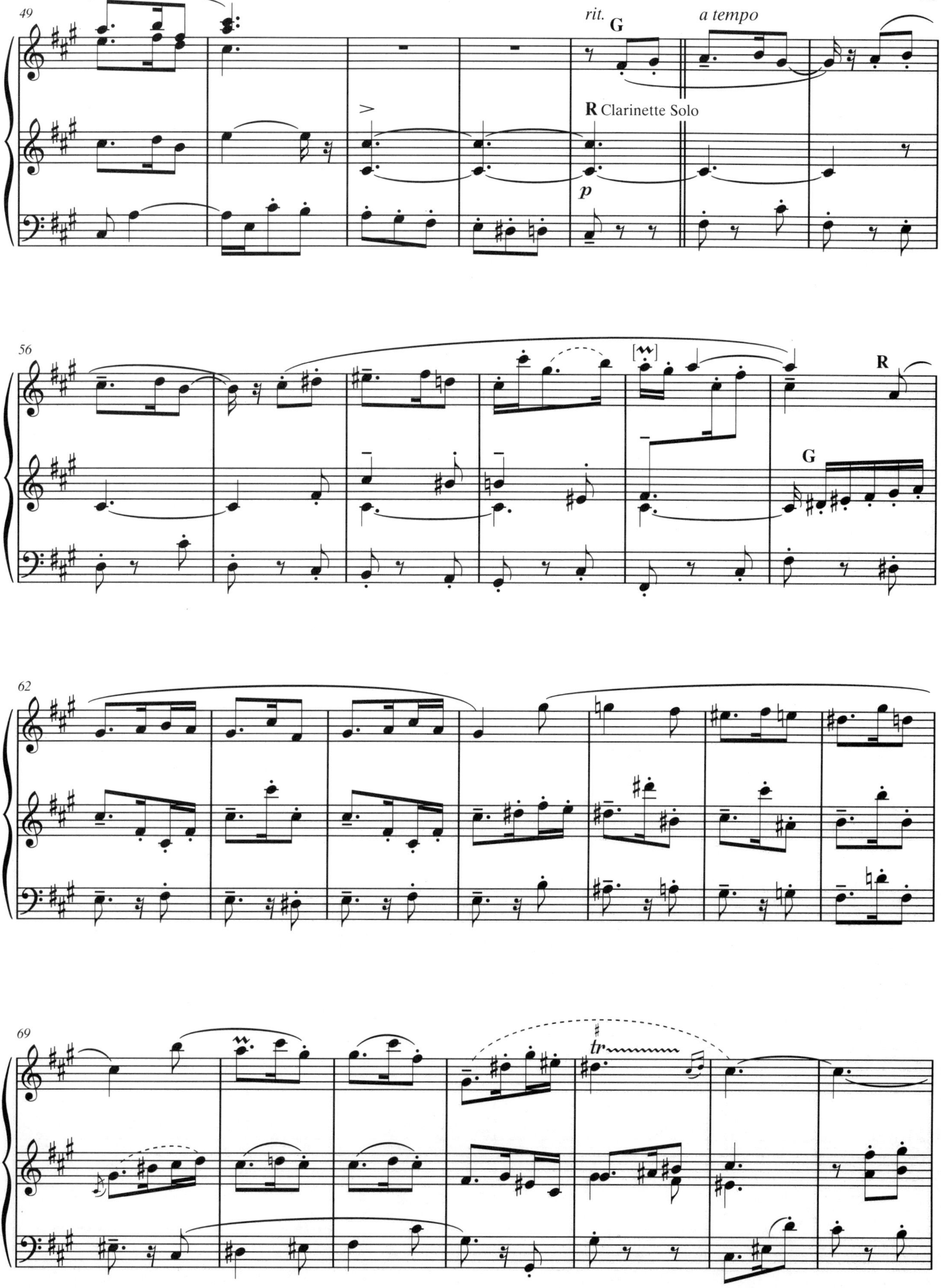
49
rit.
G
a tempo
R Clarinette Solo
p
56
R
G
62
69
tr

24

25

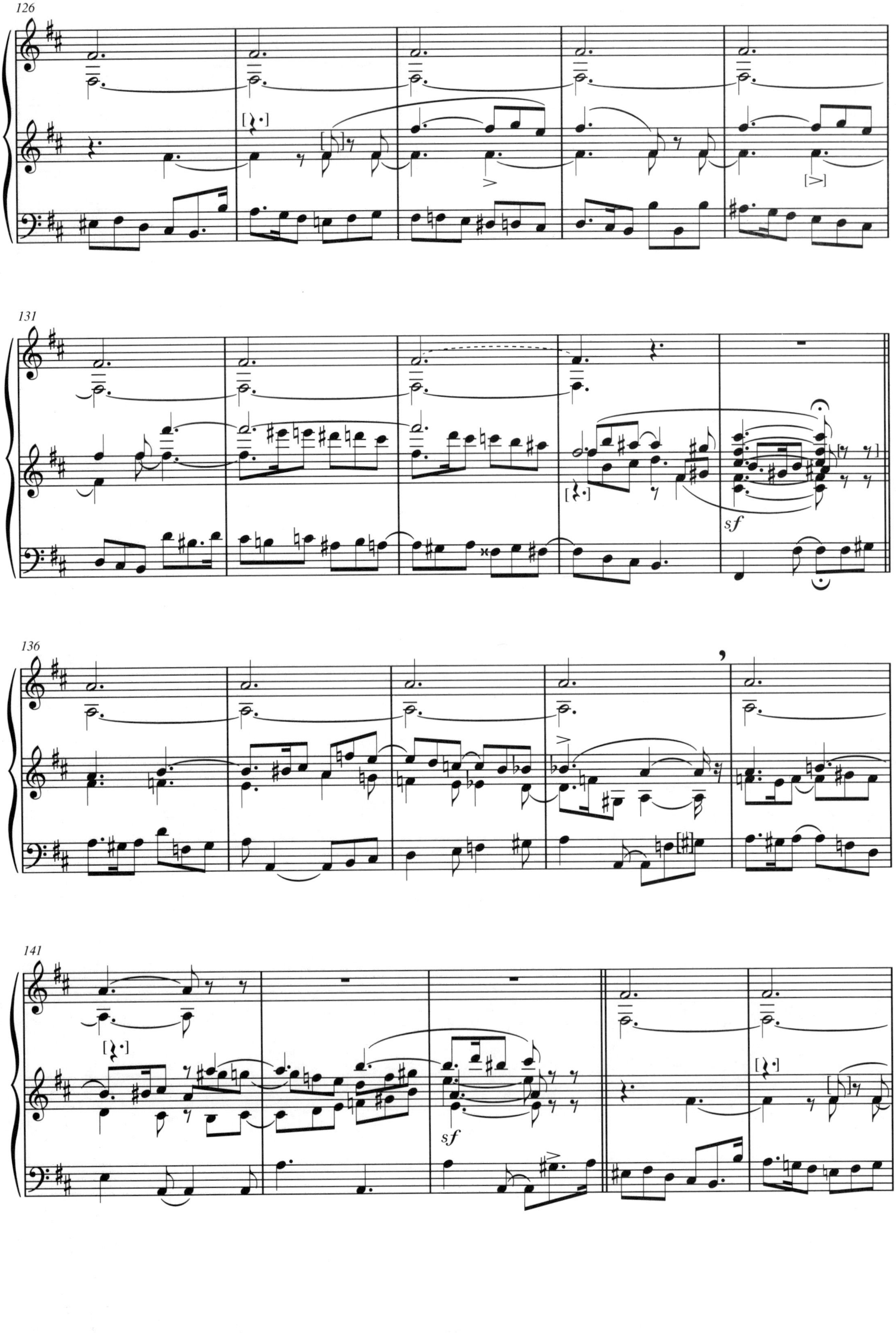
126
131
sf
136
141
sf

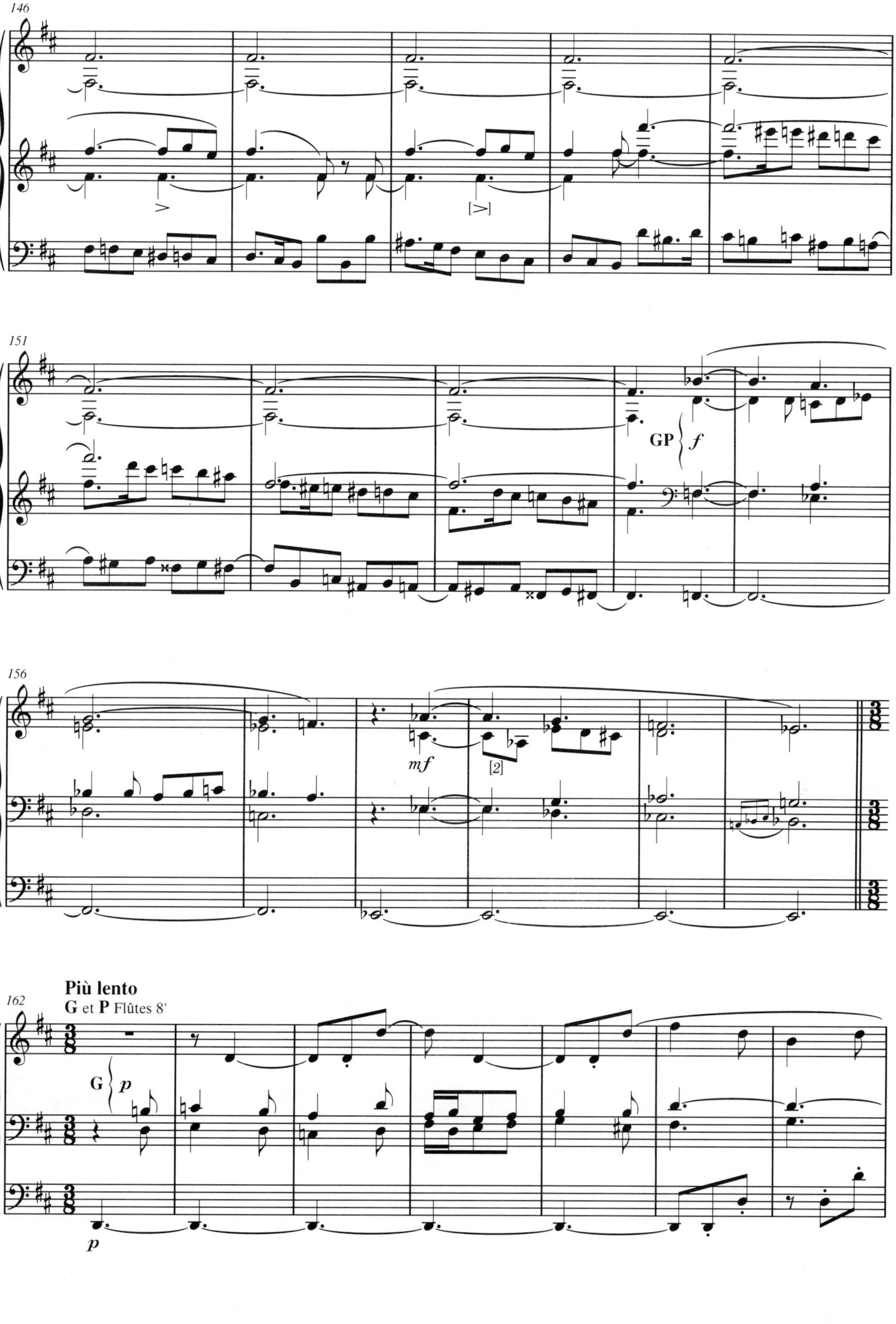
146
[>]
151
GP f
156
mf
[2]
162
Più lento
G et P Flûtes 8'
G p
p

Allegretto

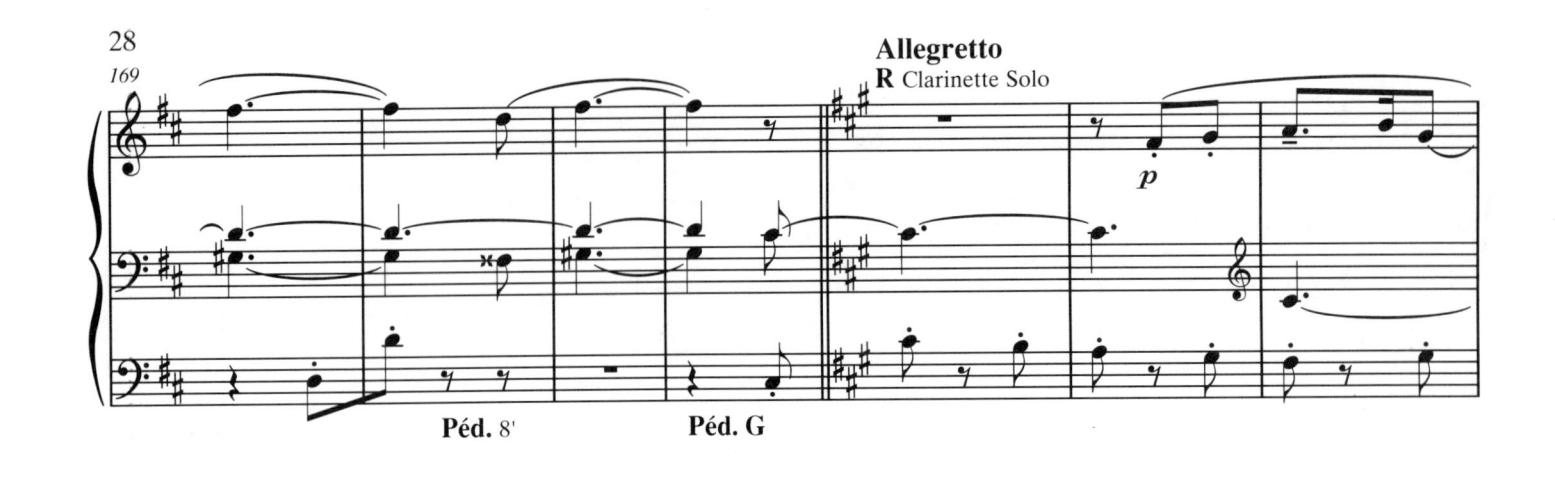

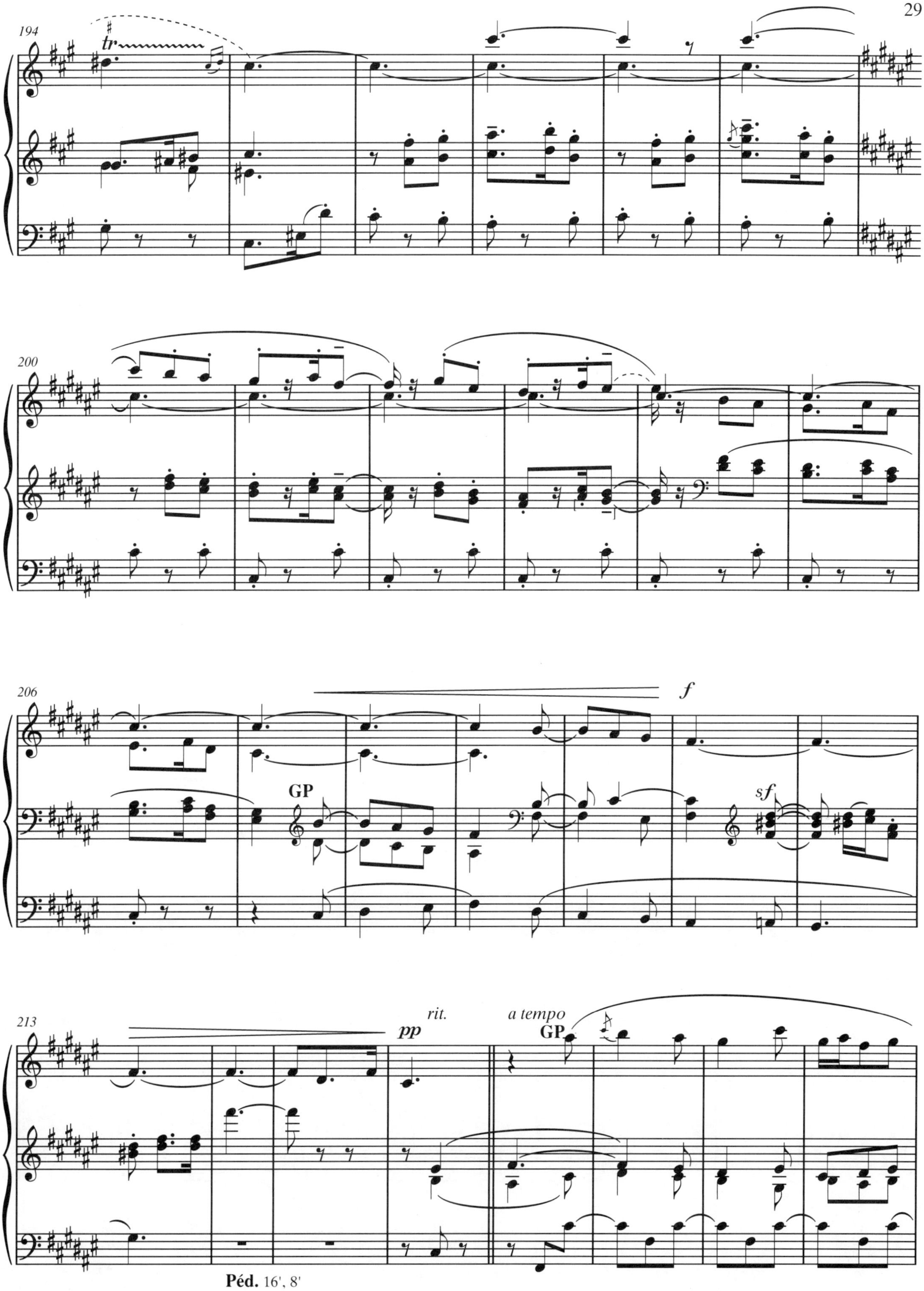
194
tr
200
206
f
GP
sf
213
pp
rit.
a tempo
GP
Péd. 16', 8'

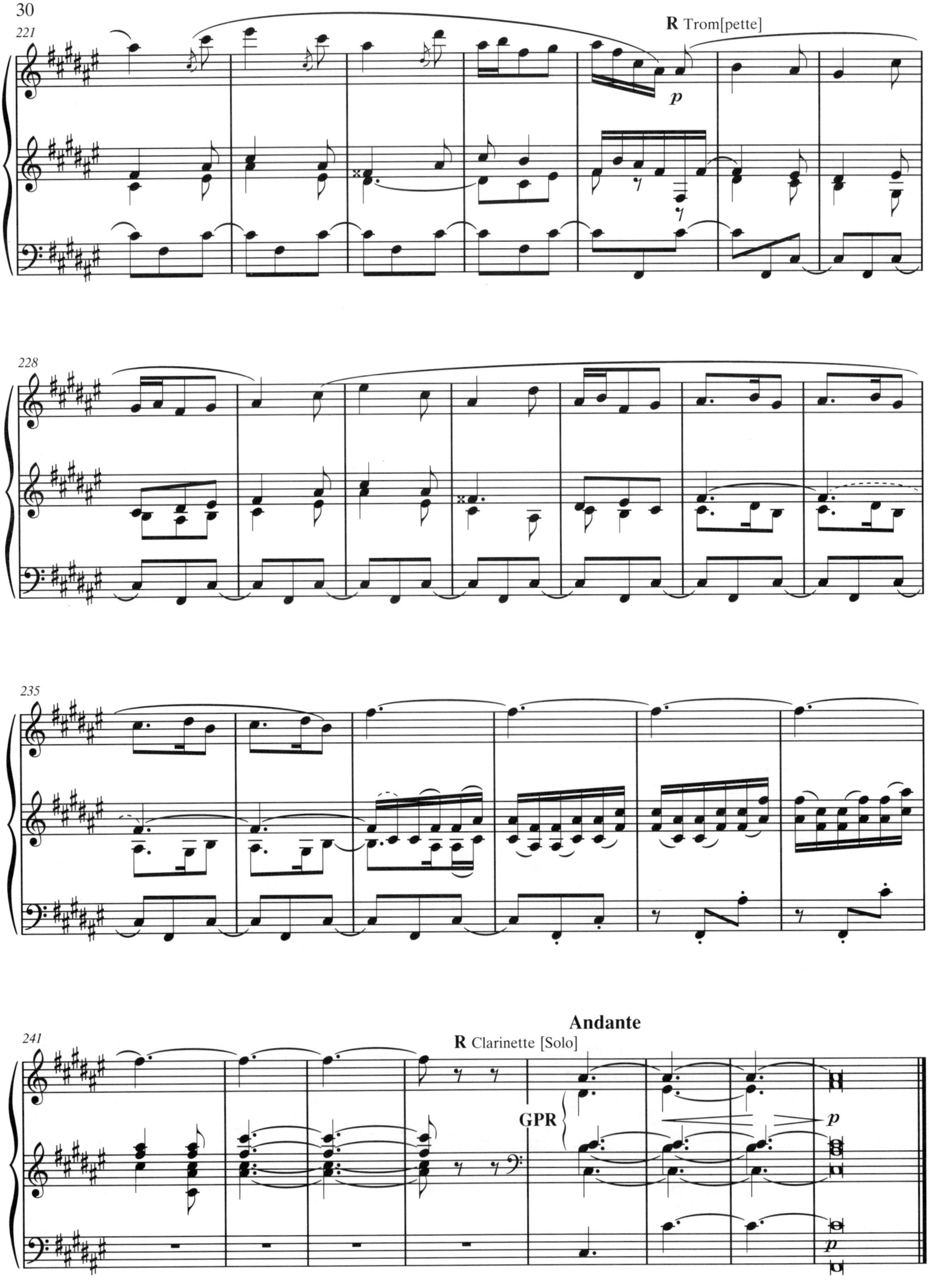
R Trom[pette]
Andante
R Clarinette [Solo]
GPR

Grand orgue: Gambes 8', Flûtes 8'
Positif: Gambes 8', Flûtes 8'
Récit: Gambes [8']
Pédale: Basses 16', 8'

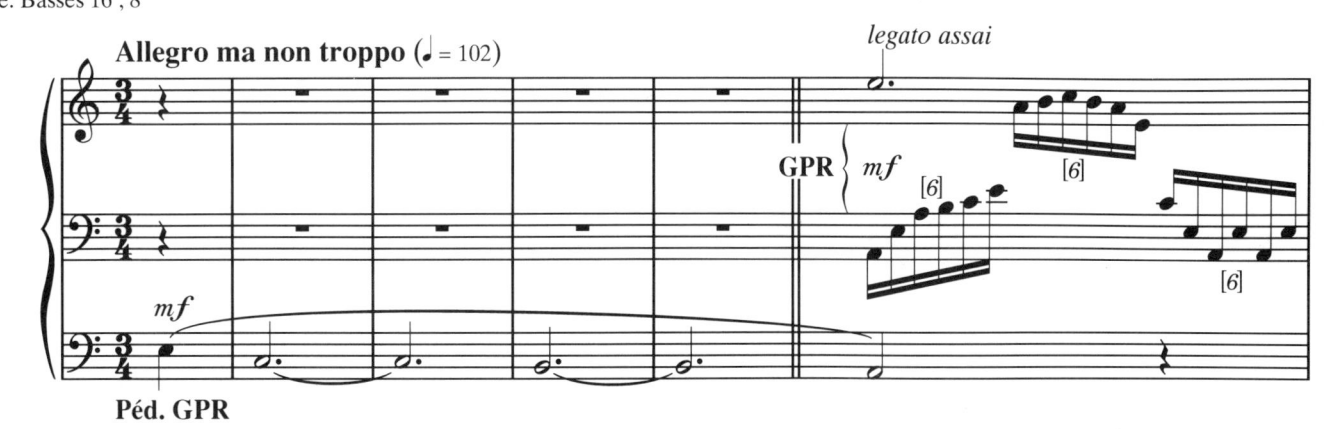

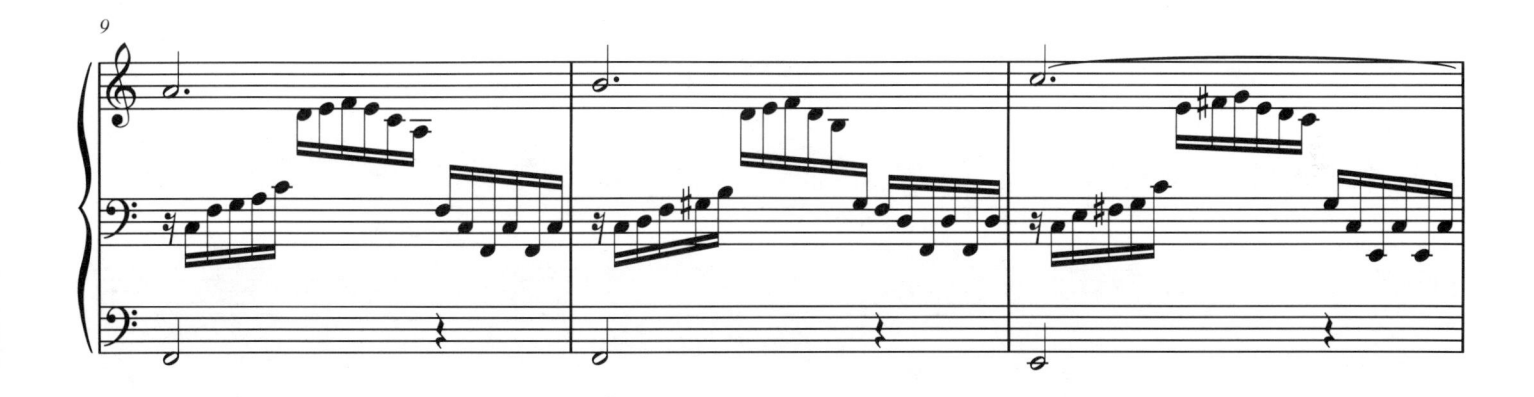

IV

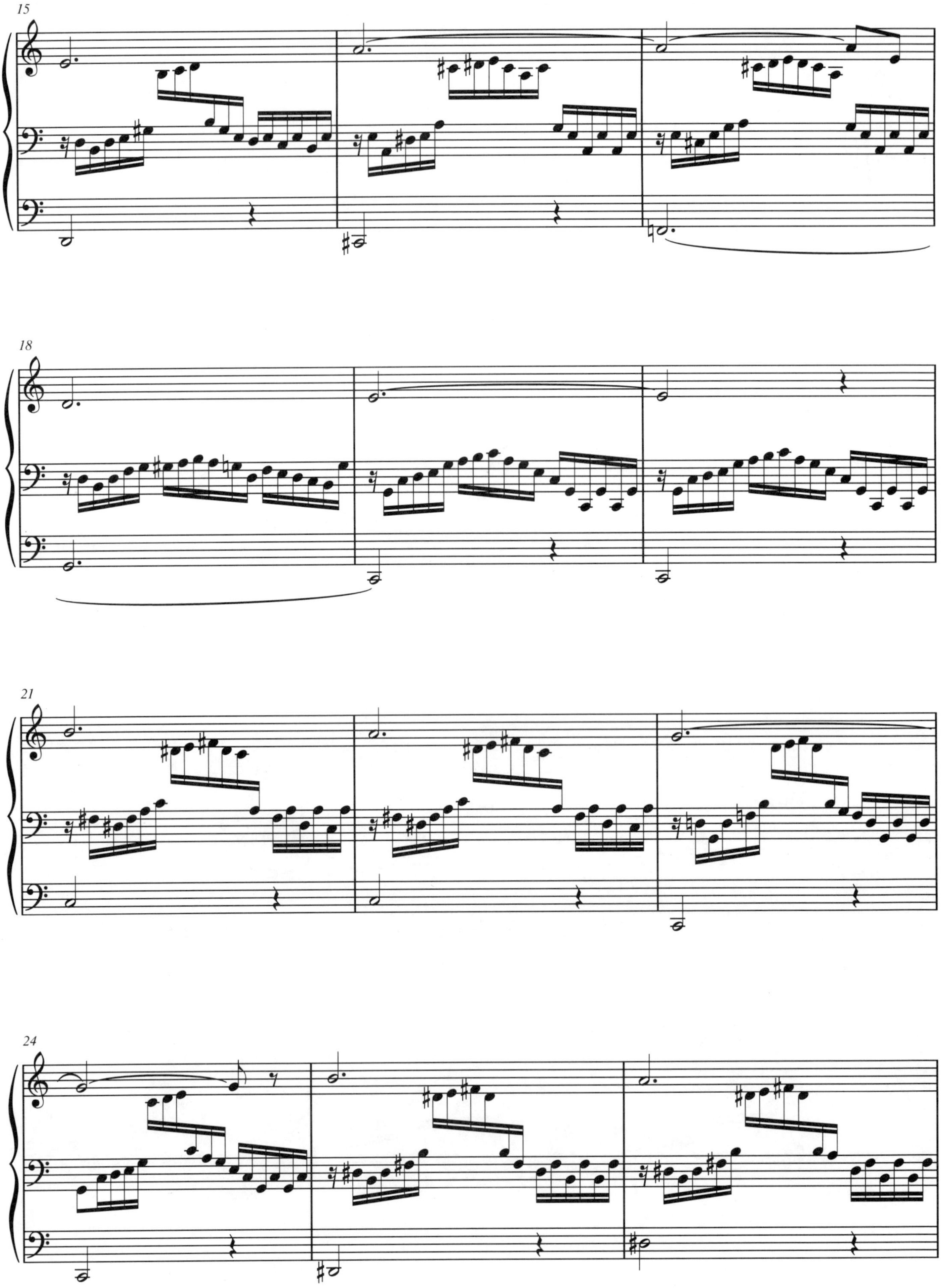
15
18
21
24

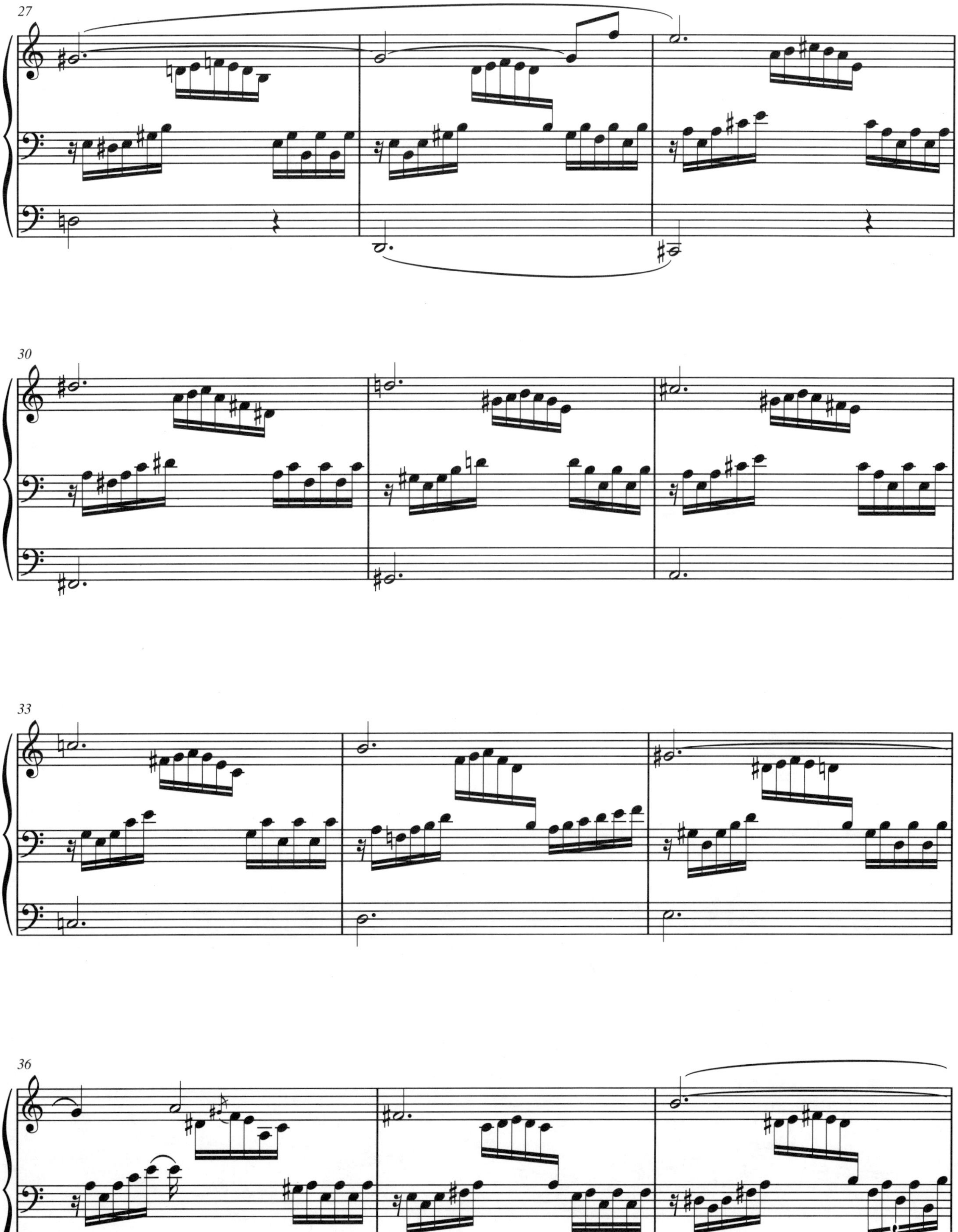
27
30
33
36

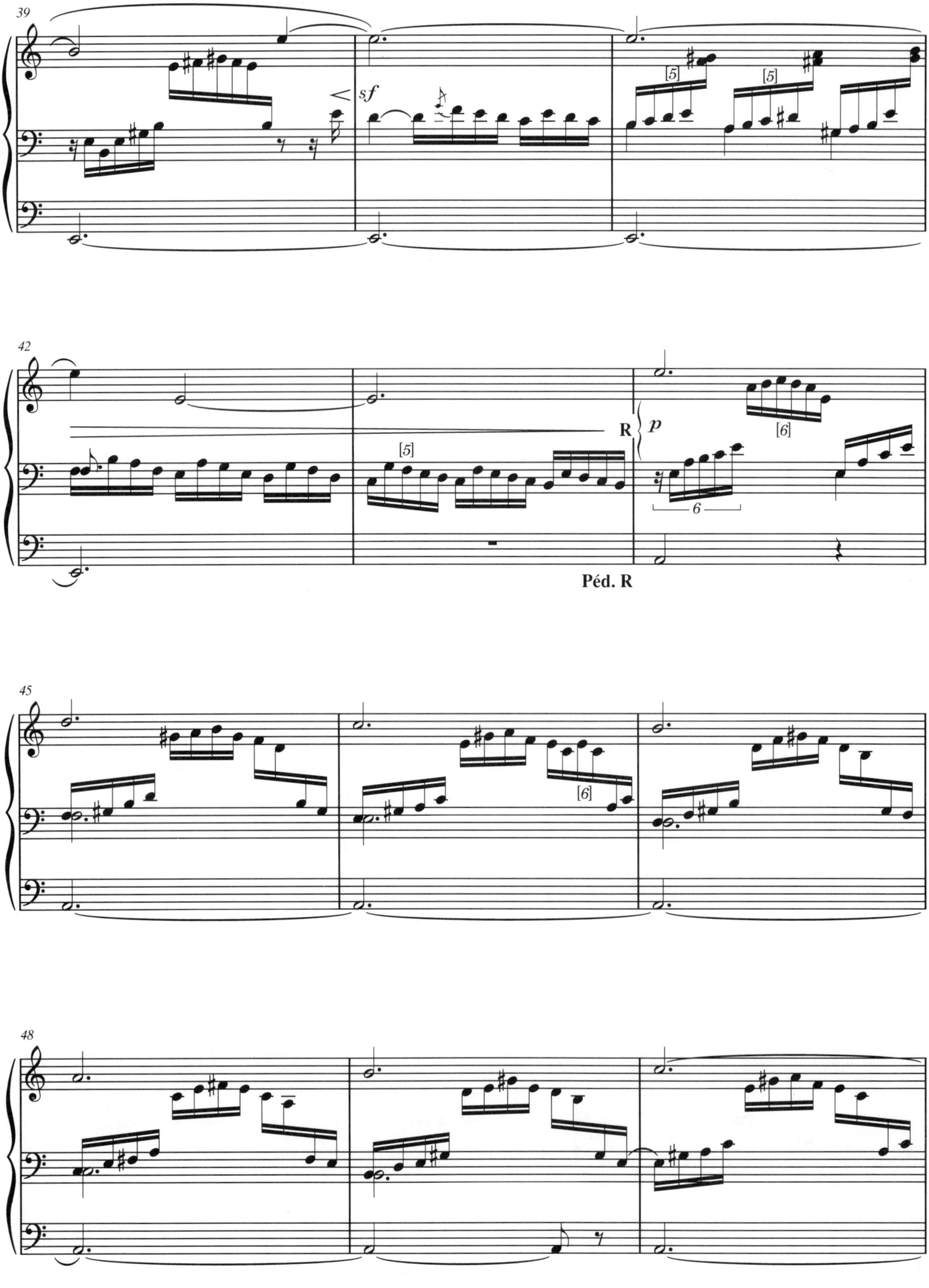
39
sf
[5]
[5]
42
[5]
R
p
[6]
6
Péd. R
45
[6]
48

35

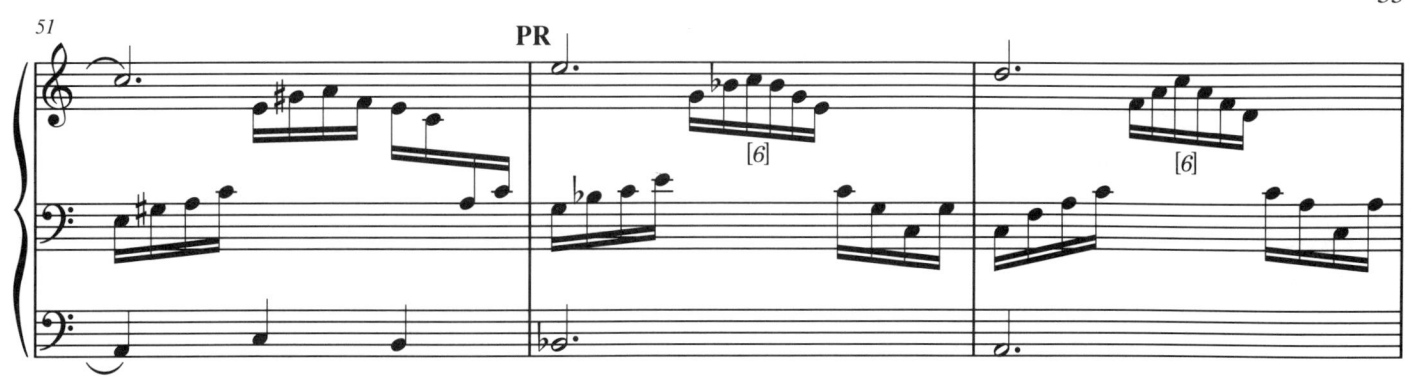

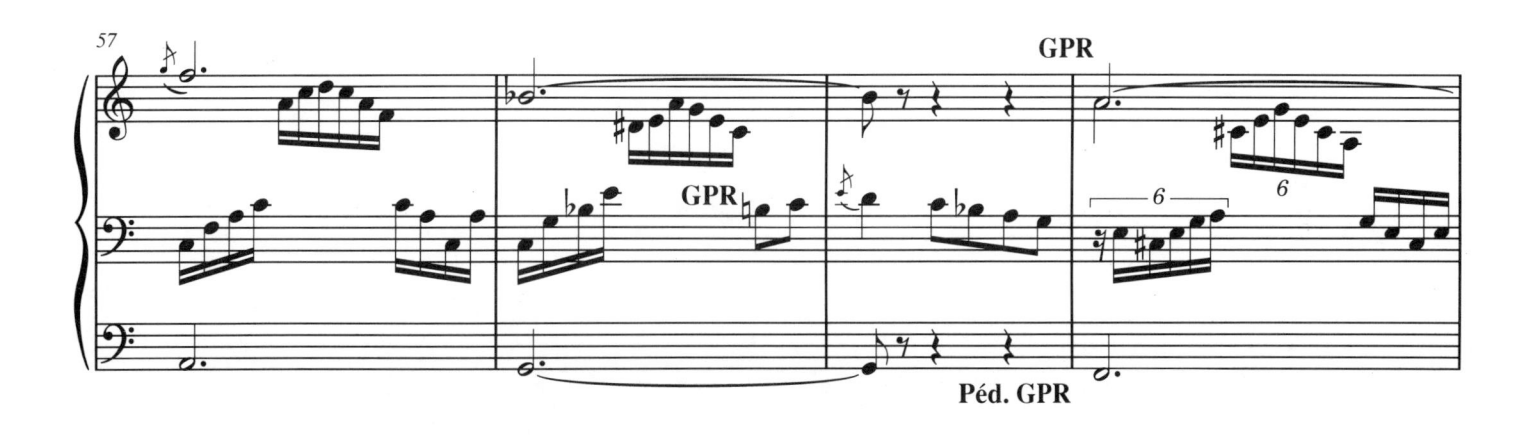

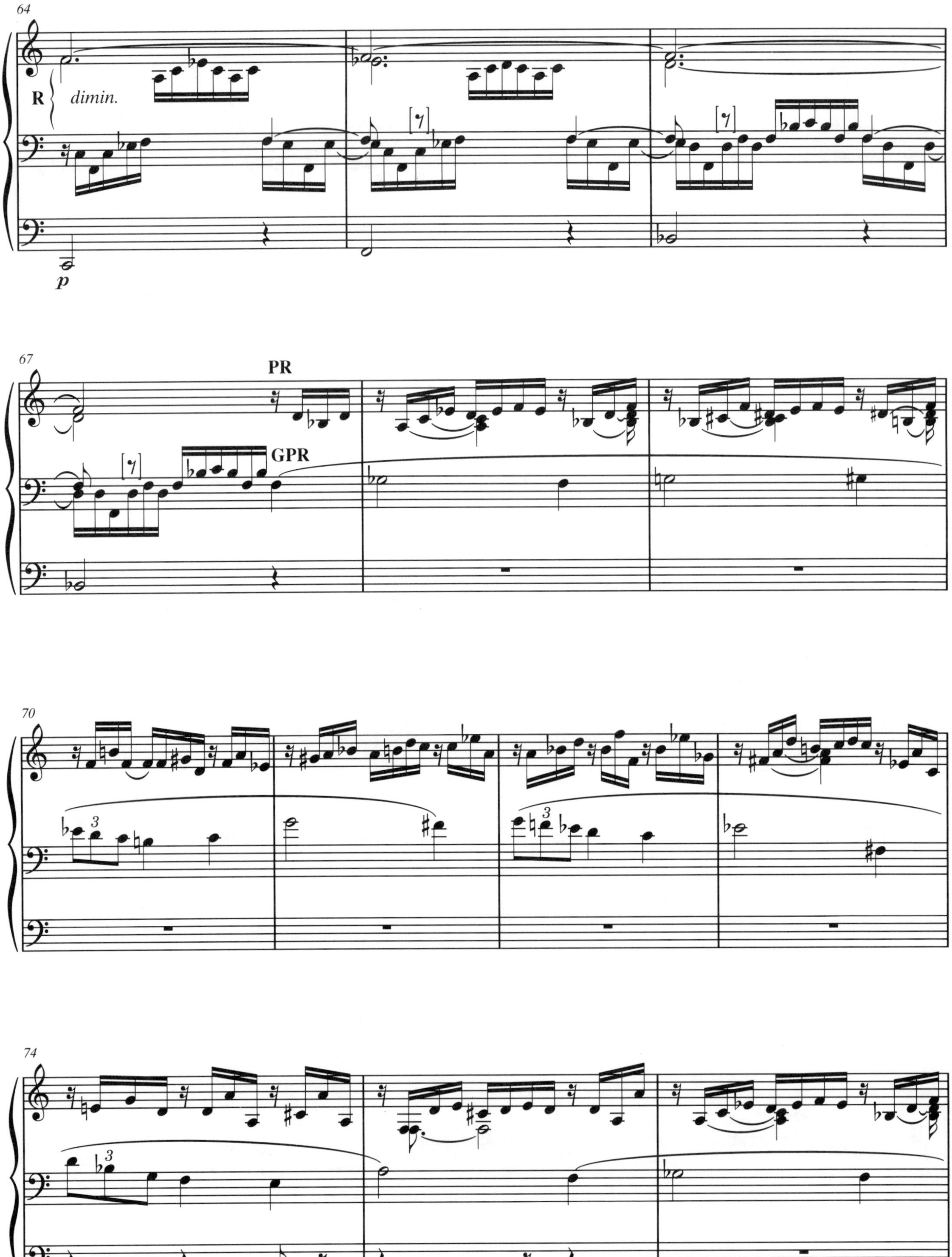
64
R
dimin.
p
67
PR
GPR
70
3
3
74
3

77
R
PR
dim.
3
81
rit.
animato
rit.
a tempo
R
pp
GPR
[Péd. R]
85
pp
R
[6]
[6]
pp
89
GPR

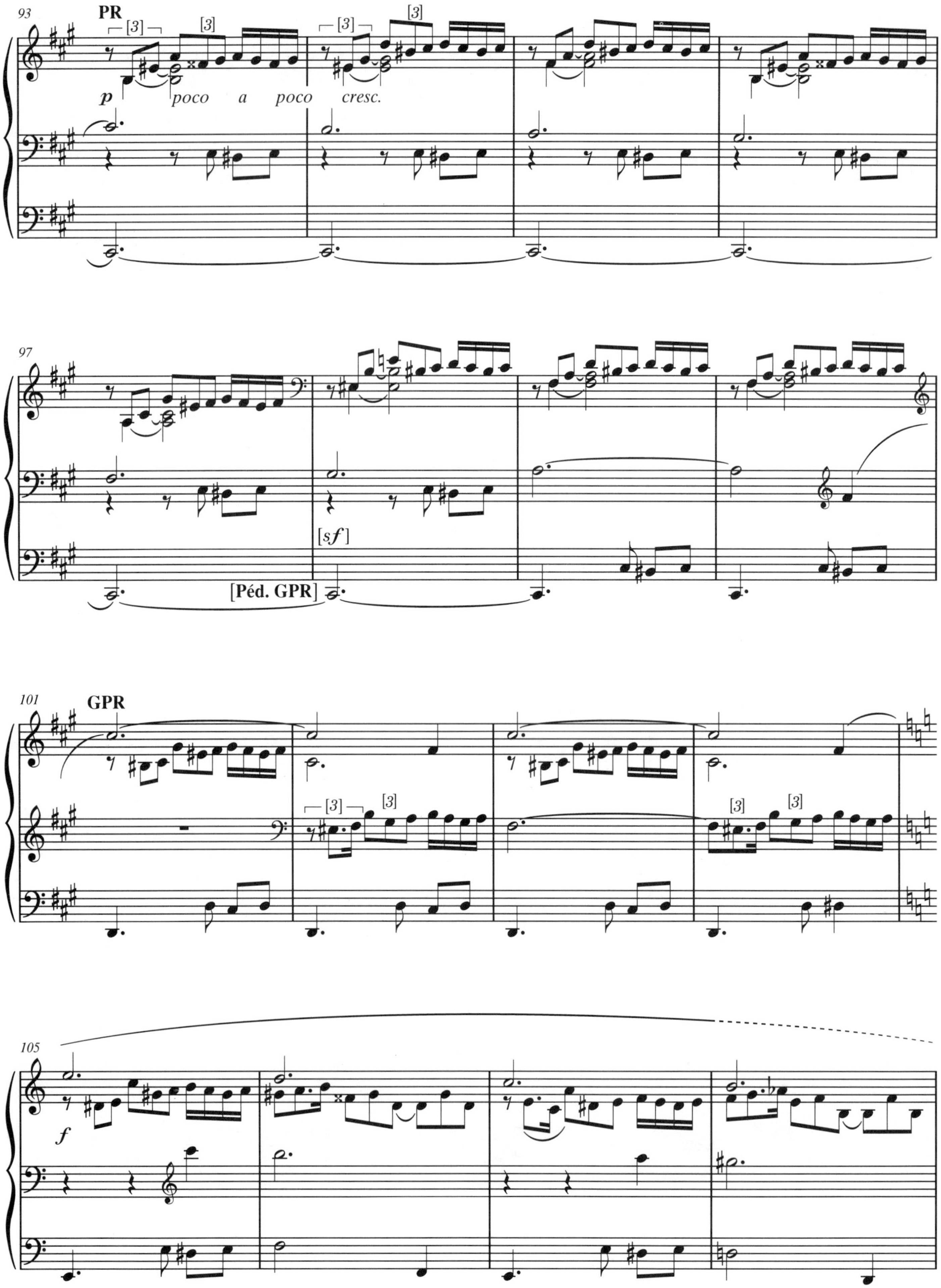
93
PR
p
poco a poco cresc.
97
[sf]
[Péd. GPR]
101
GPR
105
f

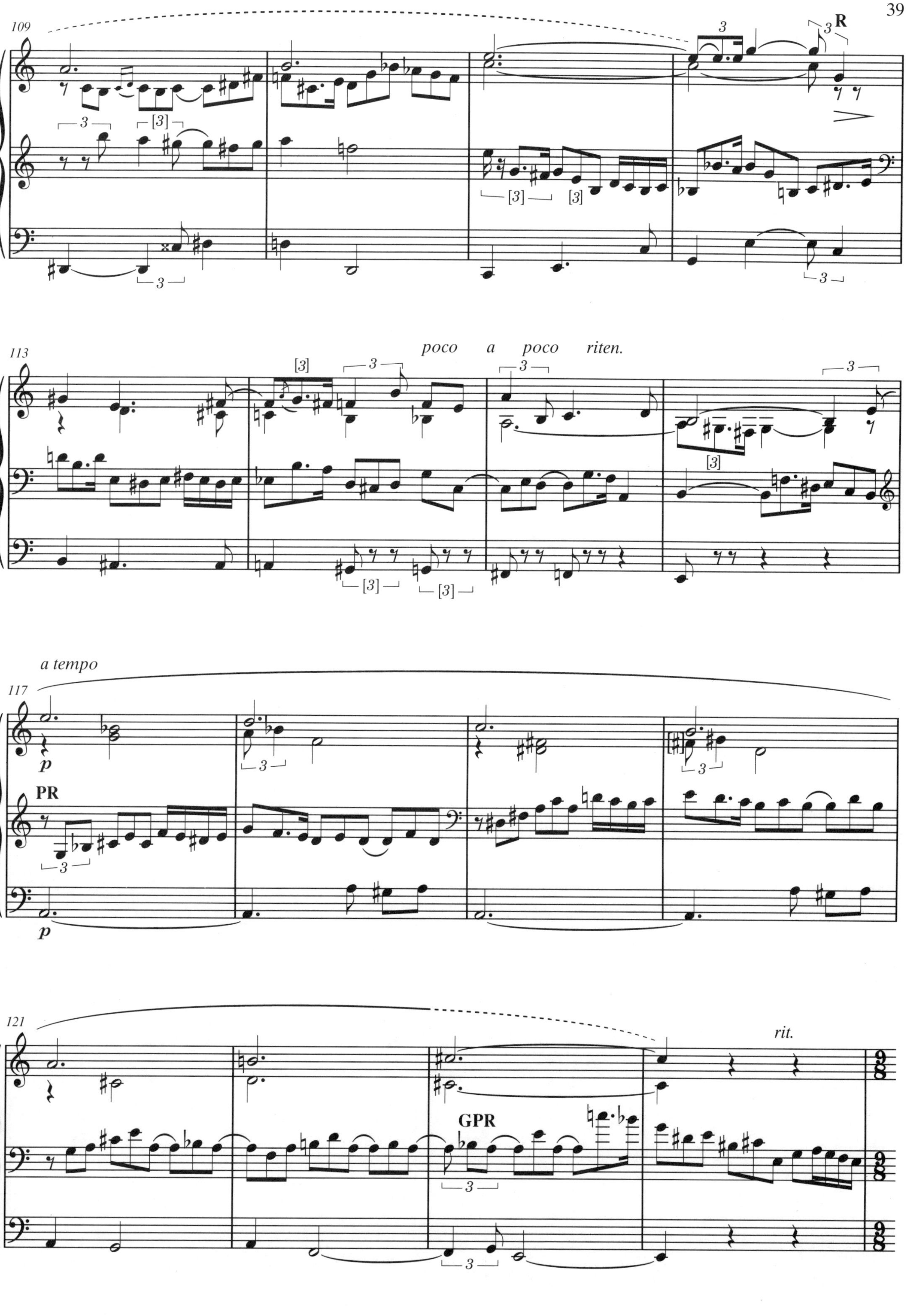
109
R
113
poco a poco riten.
a tempo
117
p
PR
121
GPR
rit.

Adagio
125
PR
f
Andante
rit.
PR
p
129
a tempo
R Flûtes 8', 4'
sf pp
133
[3]
[3]
139
f
GPR

Grand orgue: Fonds 16', 8', 4'
Positif: Gambes 8', Flûtes 8'
Récit: Flûtes 8', 4'
Pédale: Basses 16', 8'

V

42

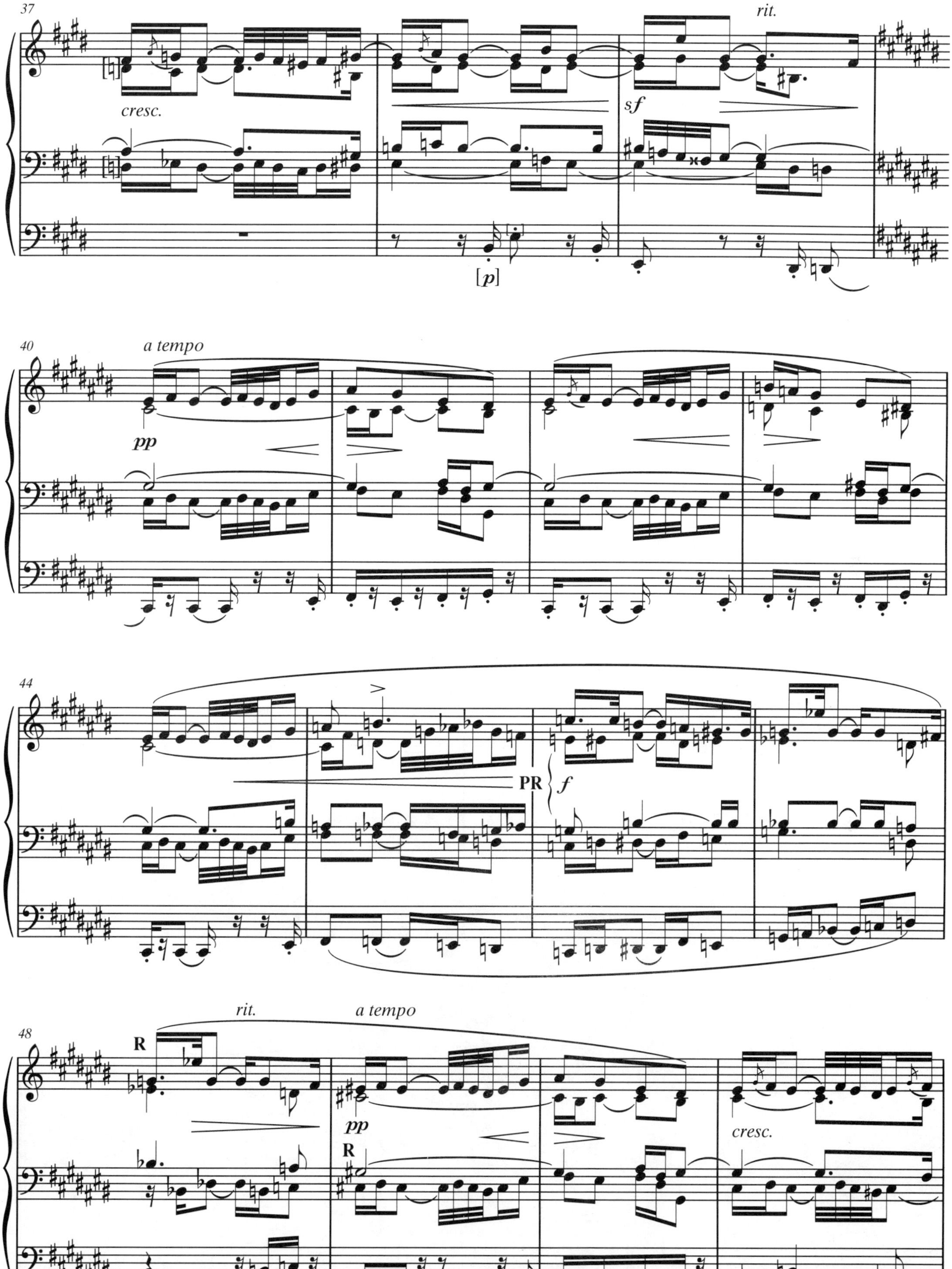
37
rit.
cresc.
sf
[p]
40
a tempo
pp
44
PR
f
48
R
rit.
a tempo
pp
R
cresc.

52
dim.
pp
ff
55
GPR
ff
Adagio molto lento
R [Gambes 8',] Voix céleste,
Bourdon 16'
61
tr
R
pp
66
sf
pp
[p]

Grand orgue:
Positif: [Fonds et] Anches 16', 8', 4'
Récit:
Pédale: [Fonds et] Anches 32', 16', 8'

VI. Finale

Allegro vivace (♩ = 138)

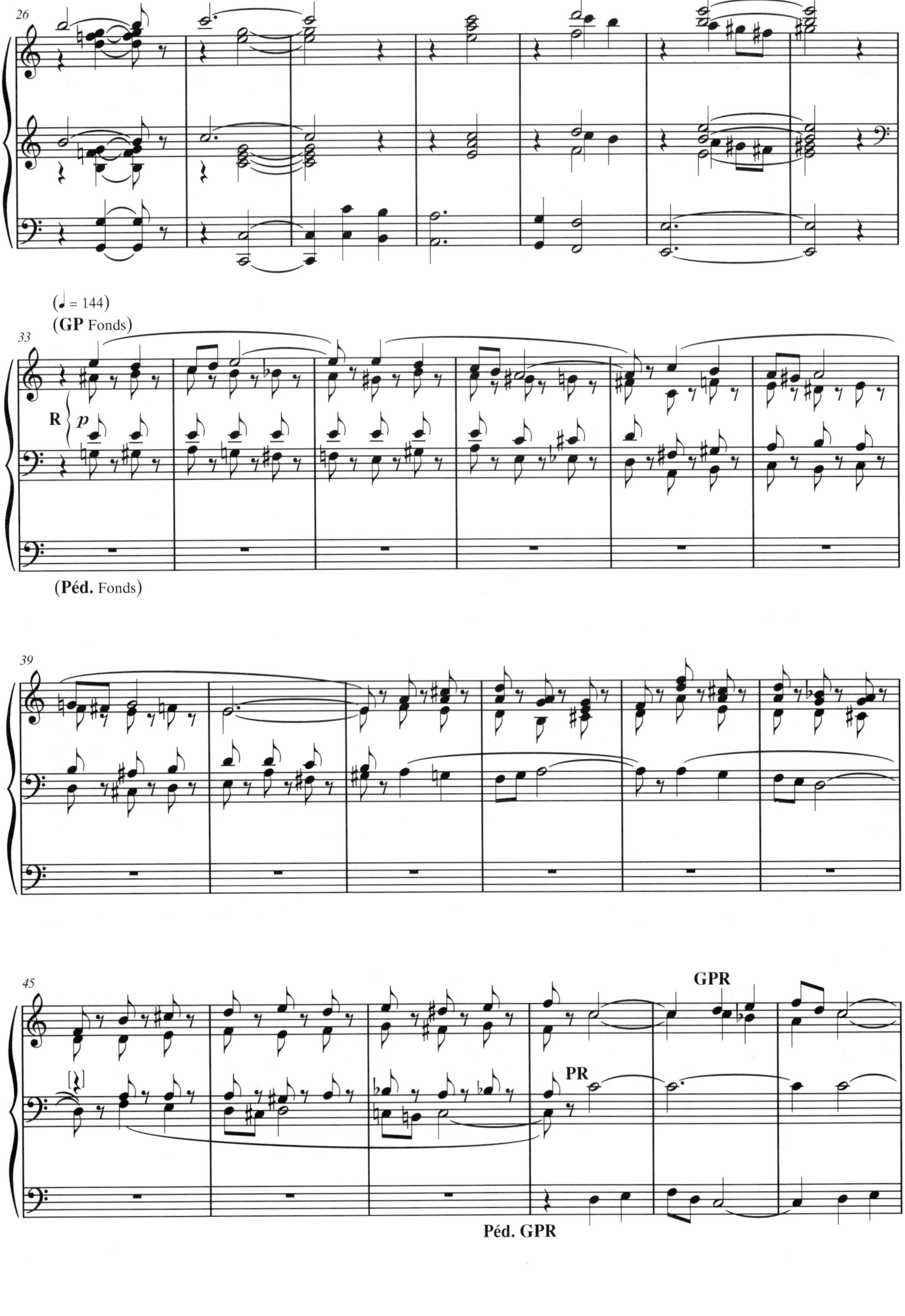
26
(♩ = 144)
(GP Fonds)
33
R
p
(Péd. Fonds)
39
45
GPR
[𝄽]
PR
Péd. GPR

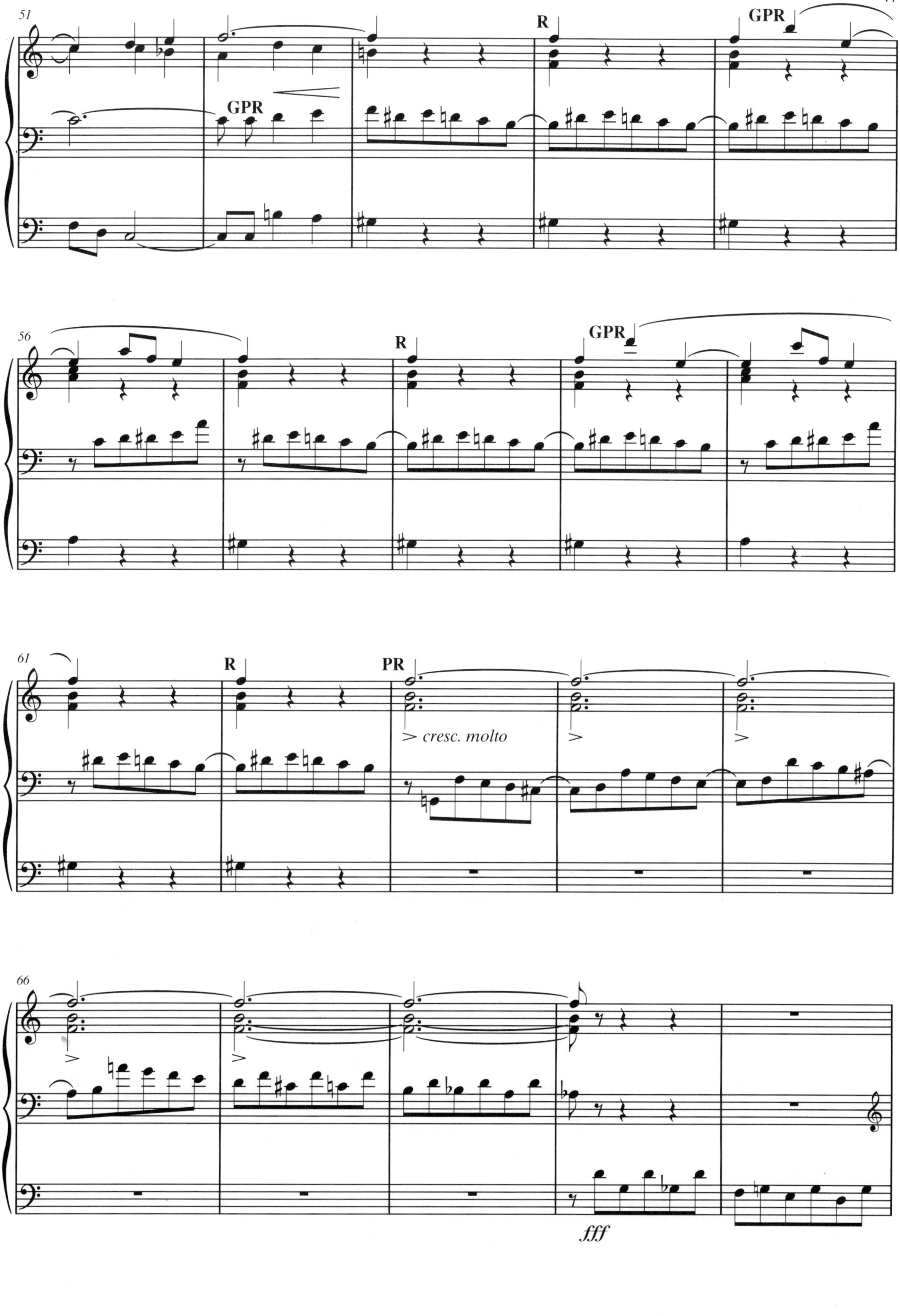
51
R
GPR
GPR
56
R
GPR
61
R
PR
cresc. molto
66
fff

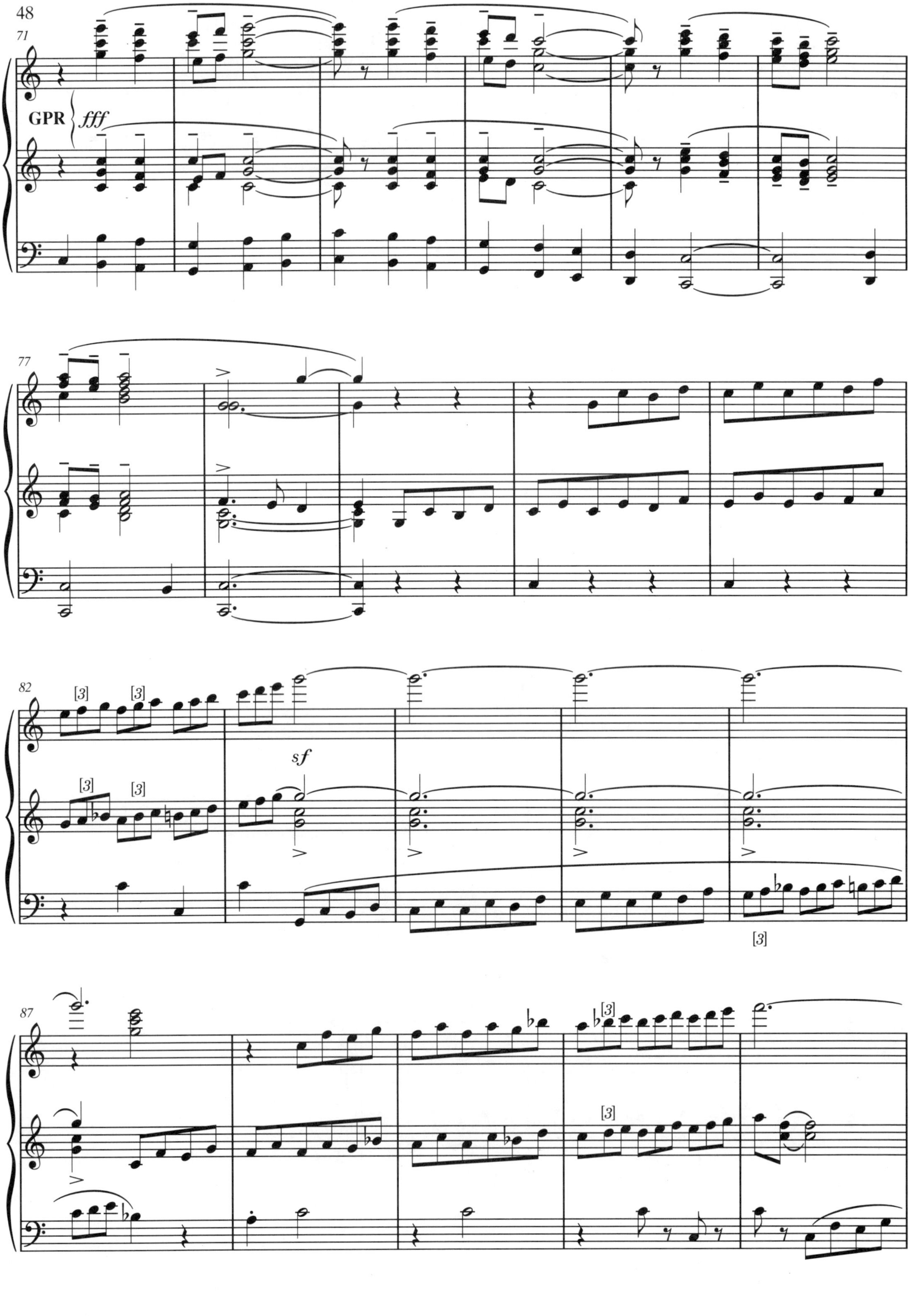
71
GPR
fff
77
82
[3]
[3]
sf
[3]
[3]
[3]
87
[3]
[3]

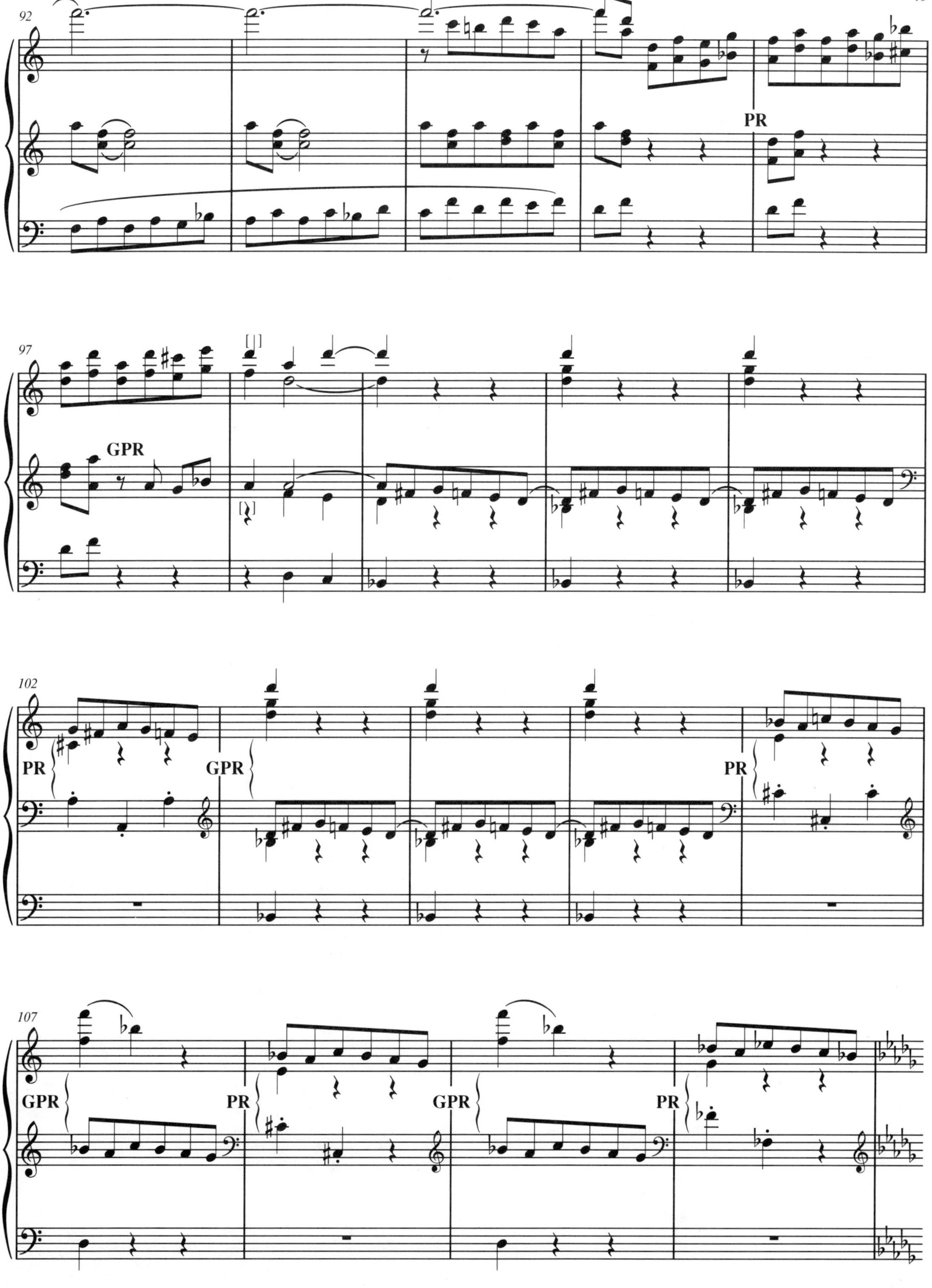
92
PR
97
GPR
102
PR
GPR
PR
107
GPR
PR
GPR
PR

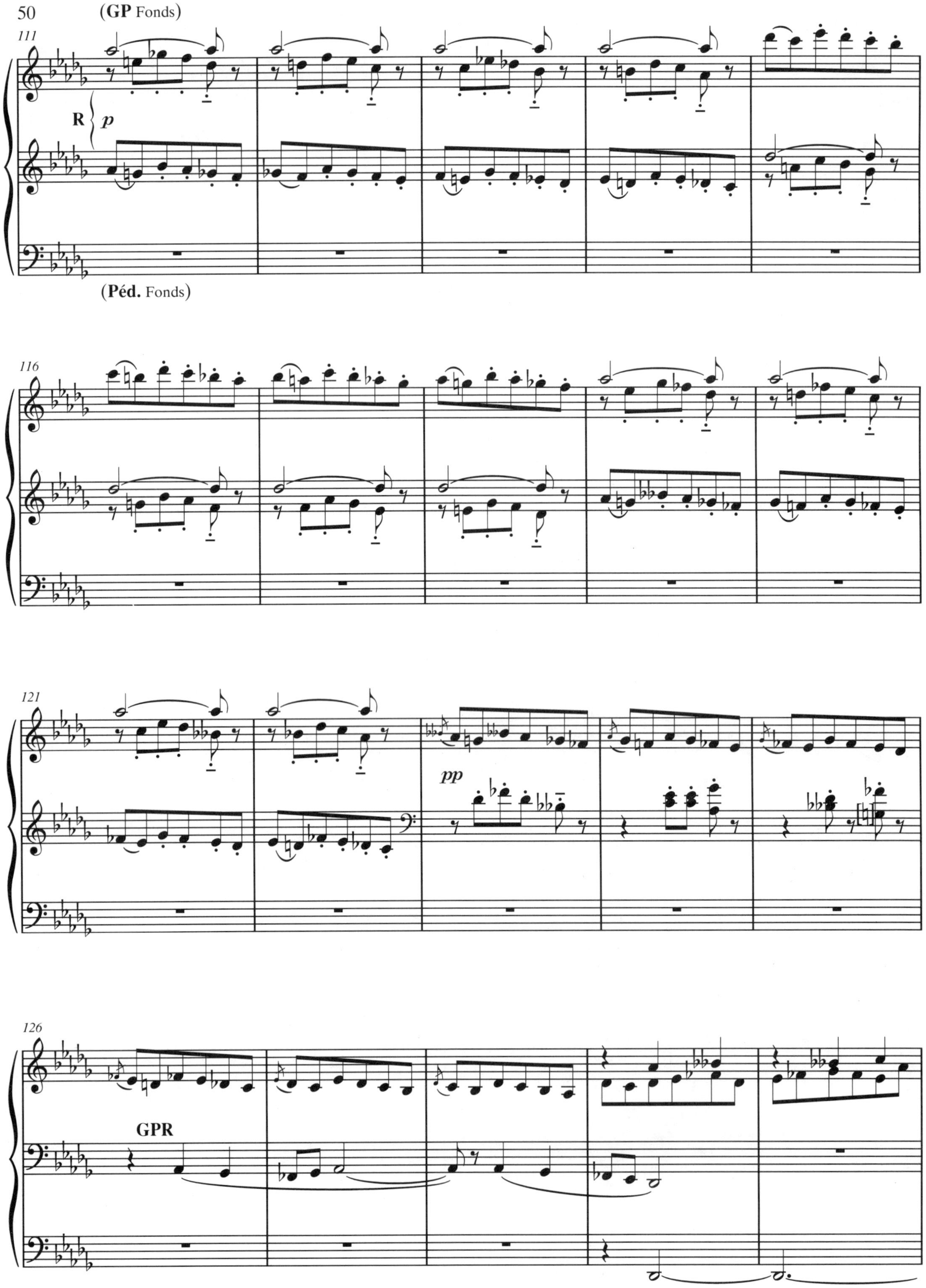
(GP Fonds)
111
R
p
(Péd. Fonds)
116
121
pp
126
GPR

51

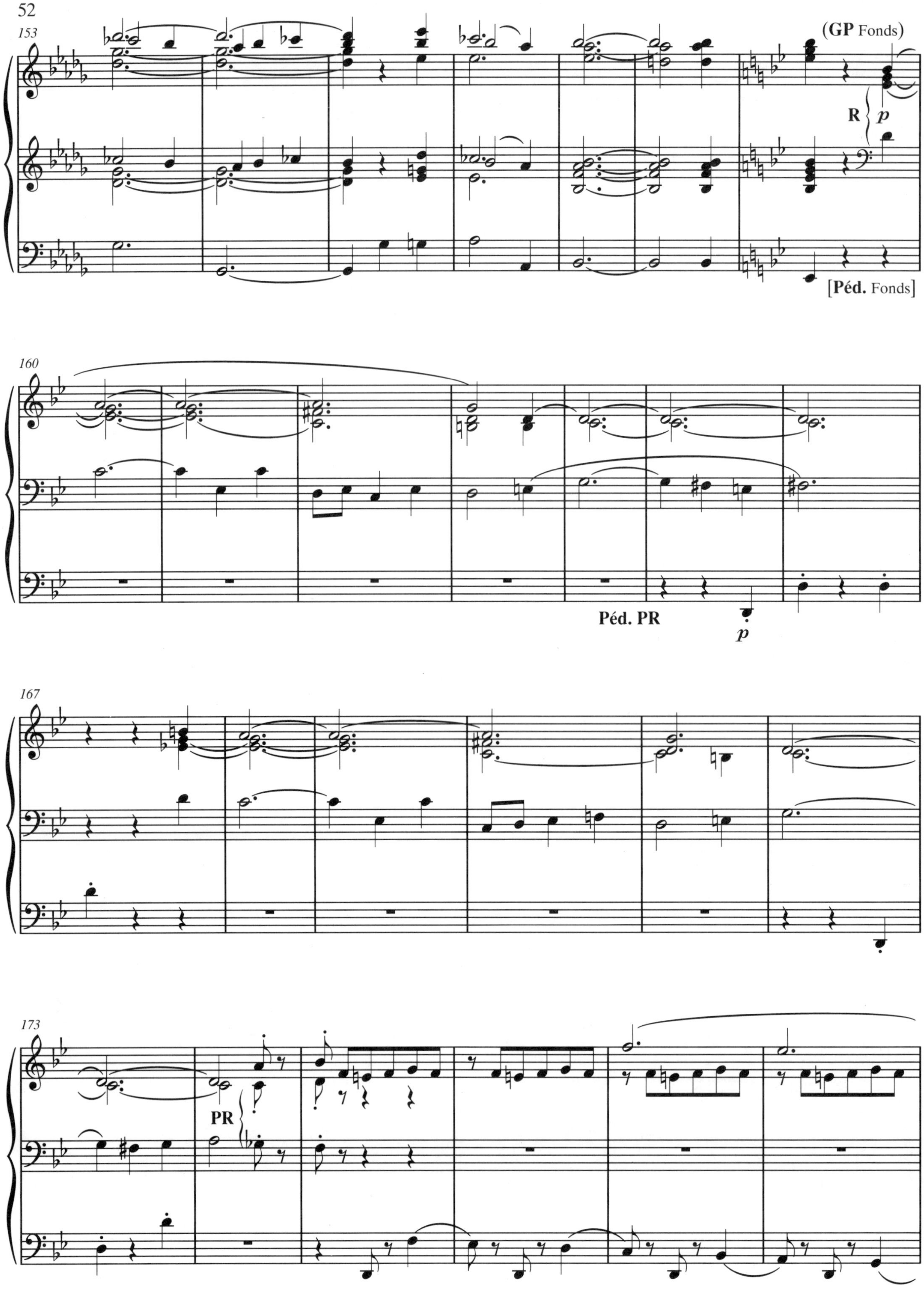
153
(GP Fonds)
R
p
[Péd. Fonds]
160
Péd. PR
p
167
173
PR

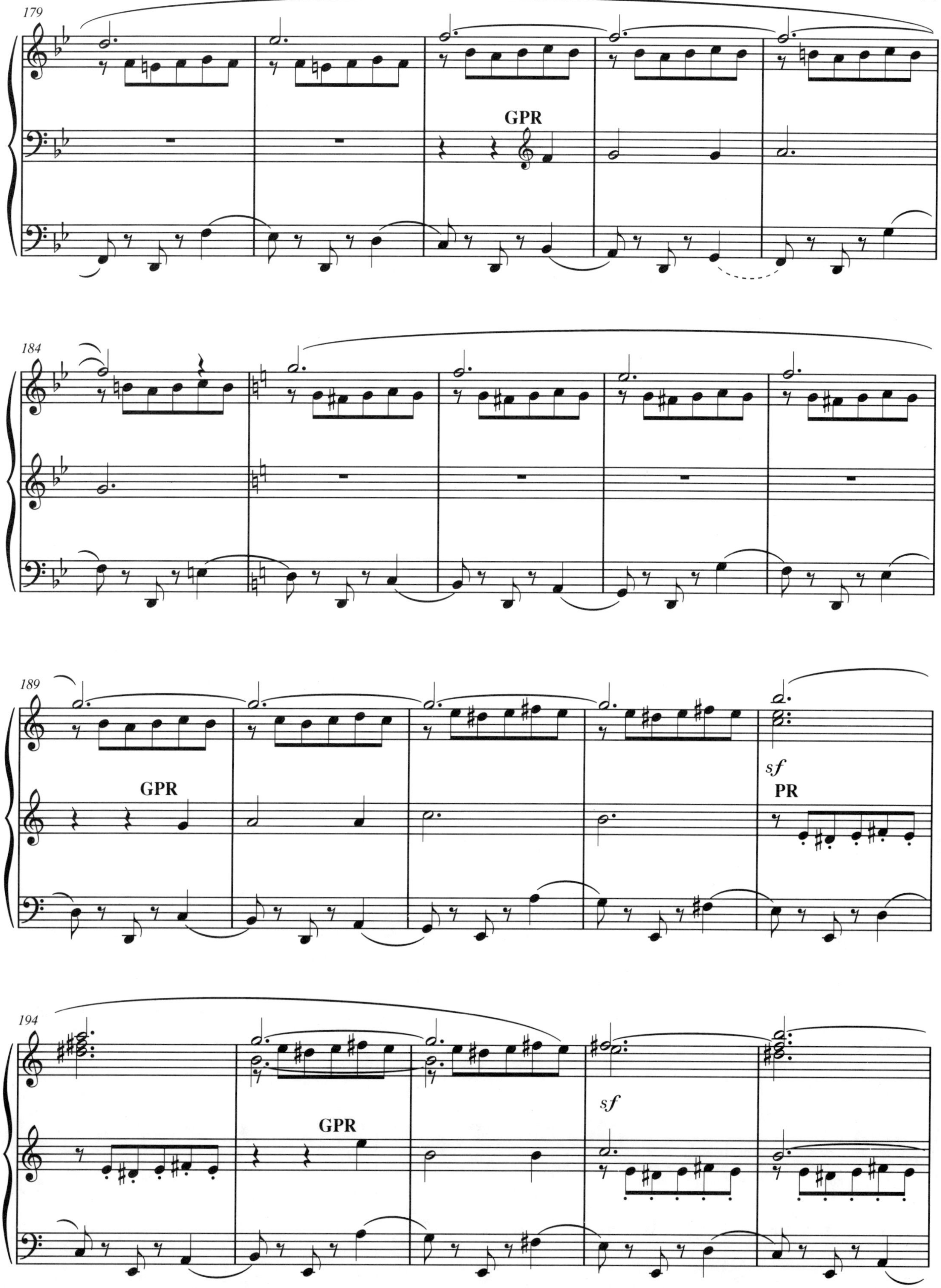
179
GPR
184
189
GPR
sf
PR
194
GPR
sf

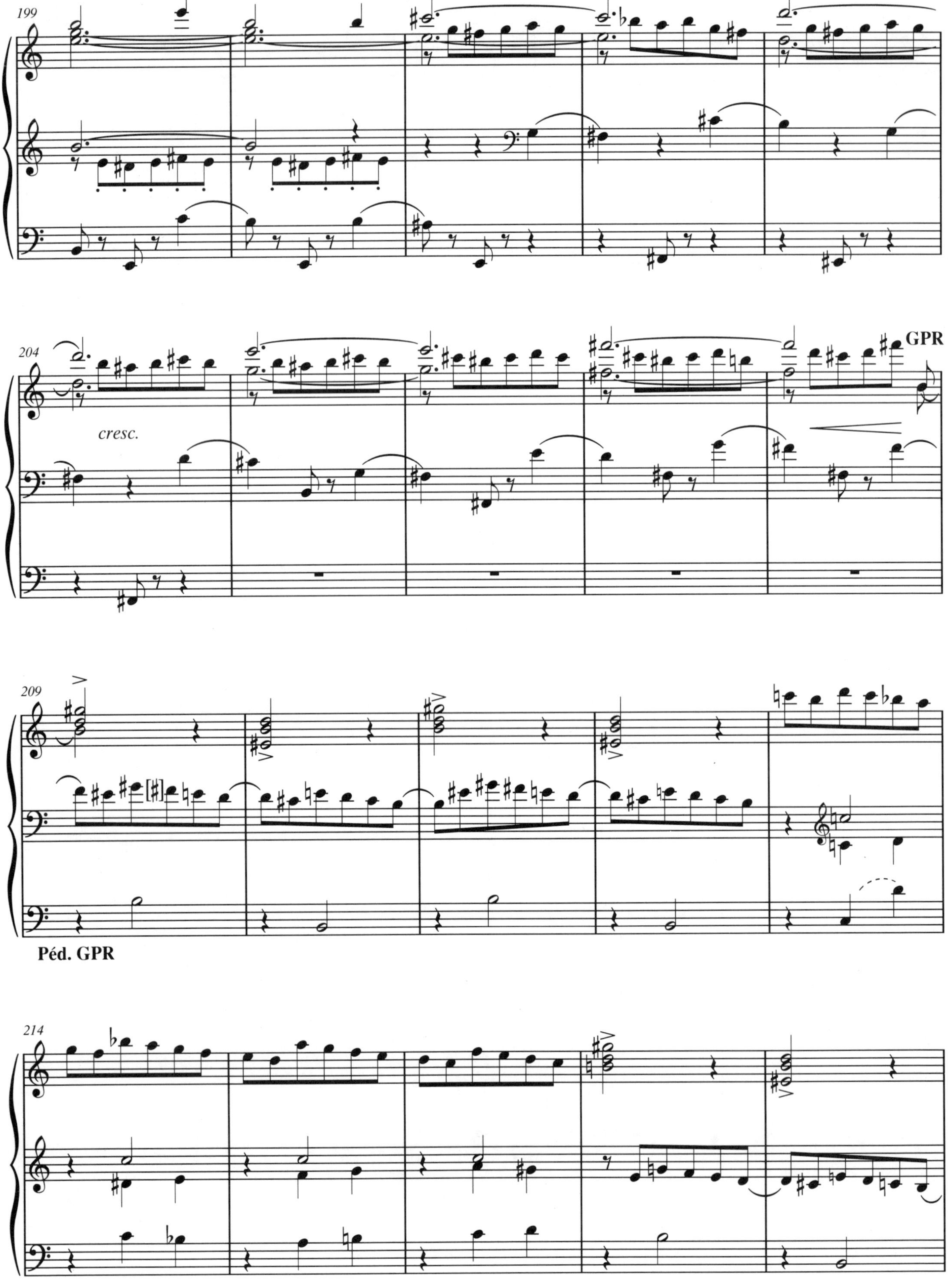
199
204
cresc.
GPR
209
Péd. GPR
214

55

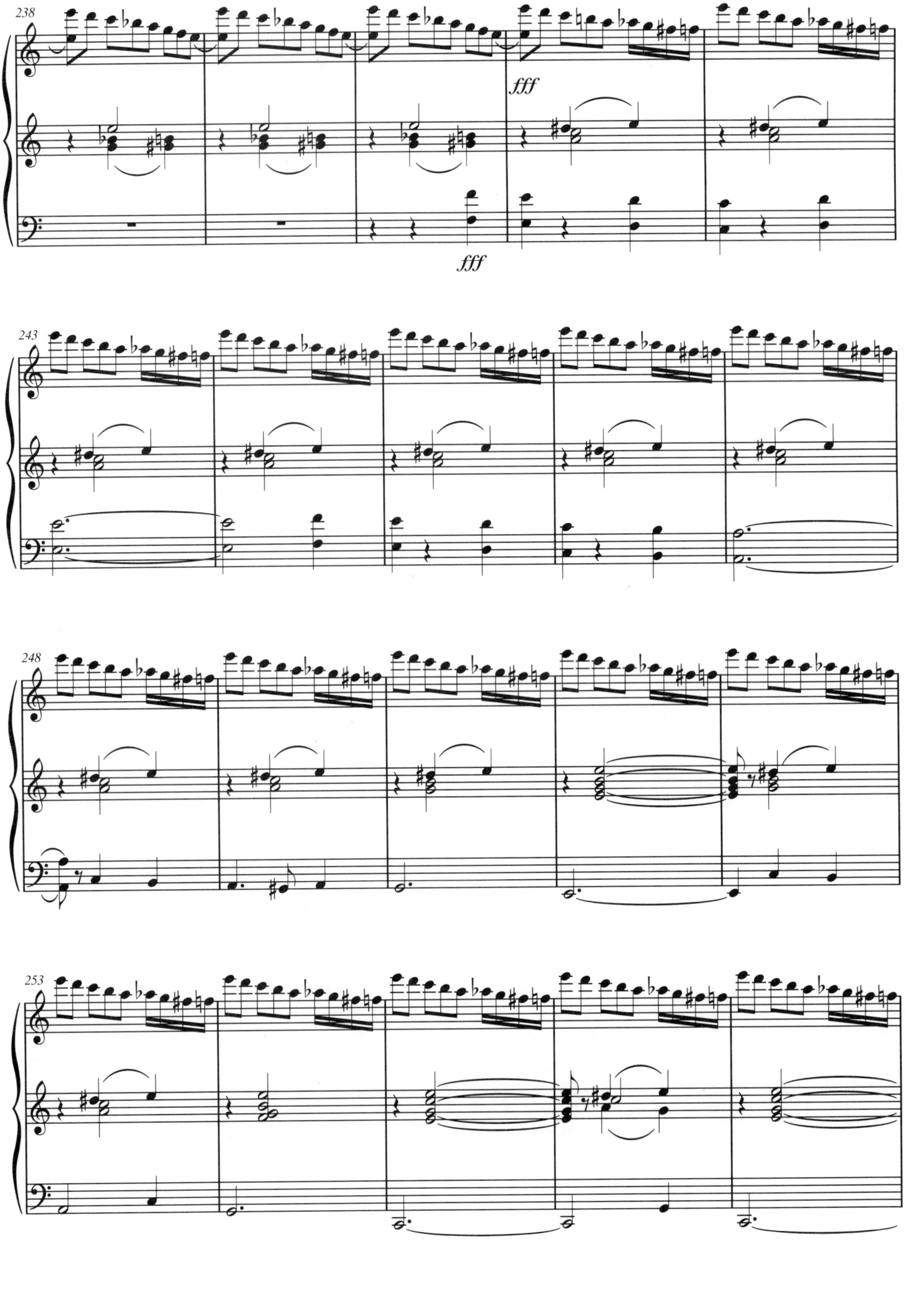
238
fff
fff
243
248
253

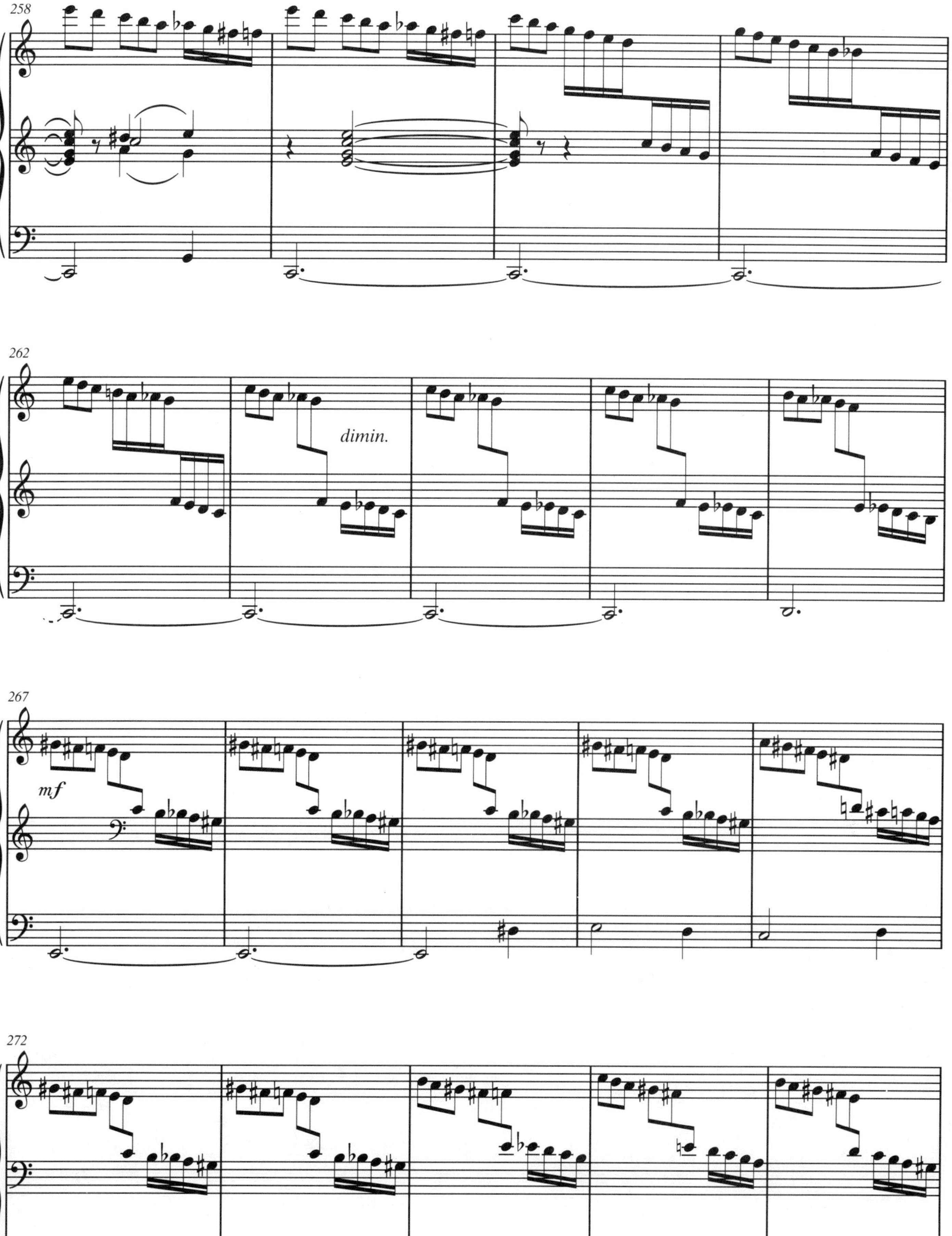
258
262
dimin.
267
mf
272

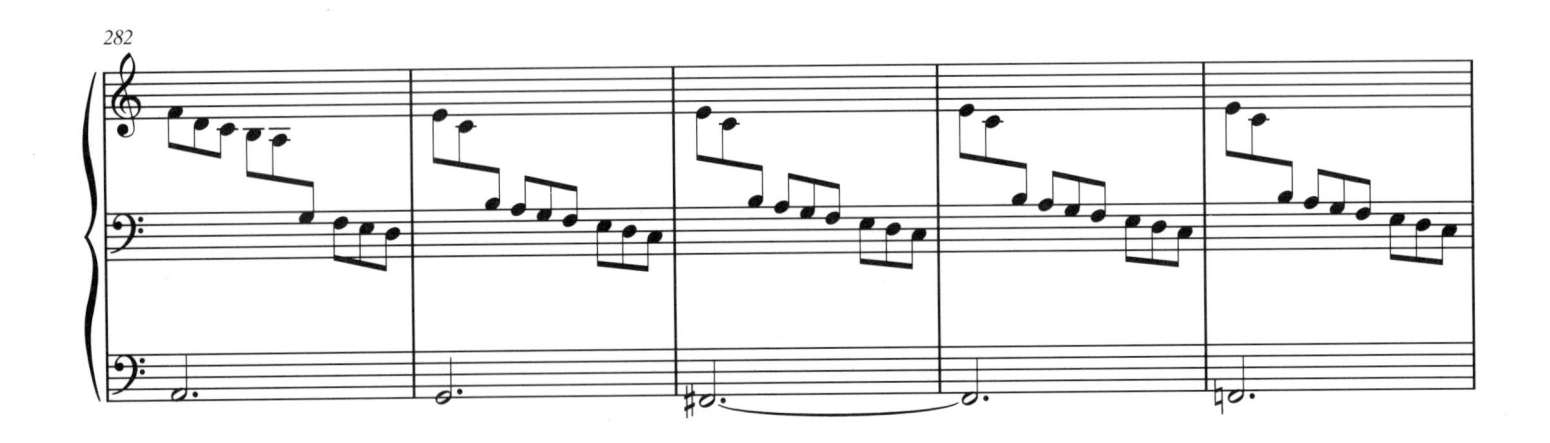

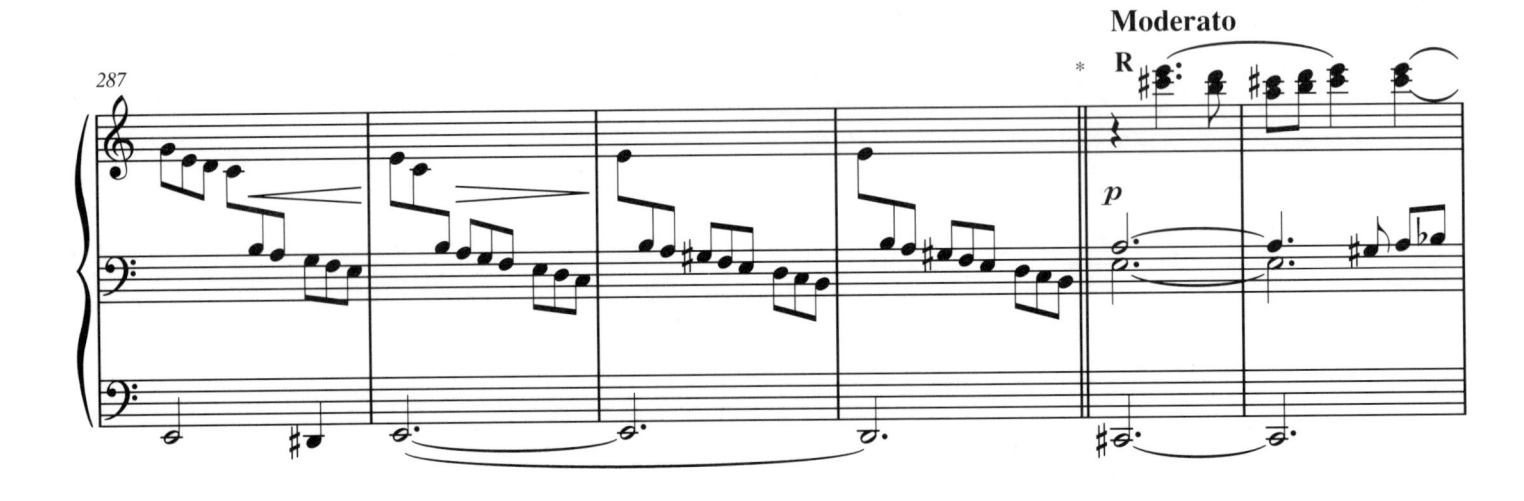

*See Critical Notes.

299
PR
rit.
GPR
[a tempo]
305
rit. molto
crescendo
3
fff
311
a tempo, a piacere
315

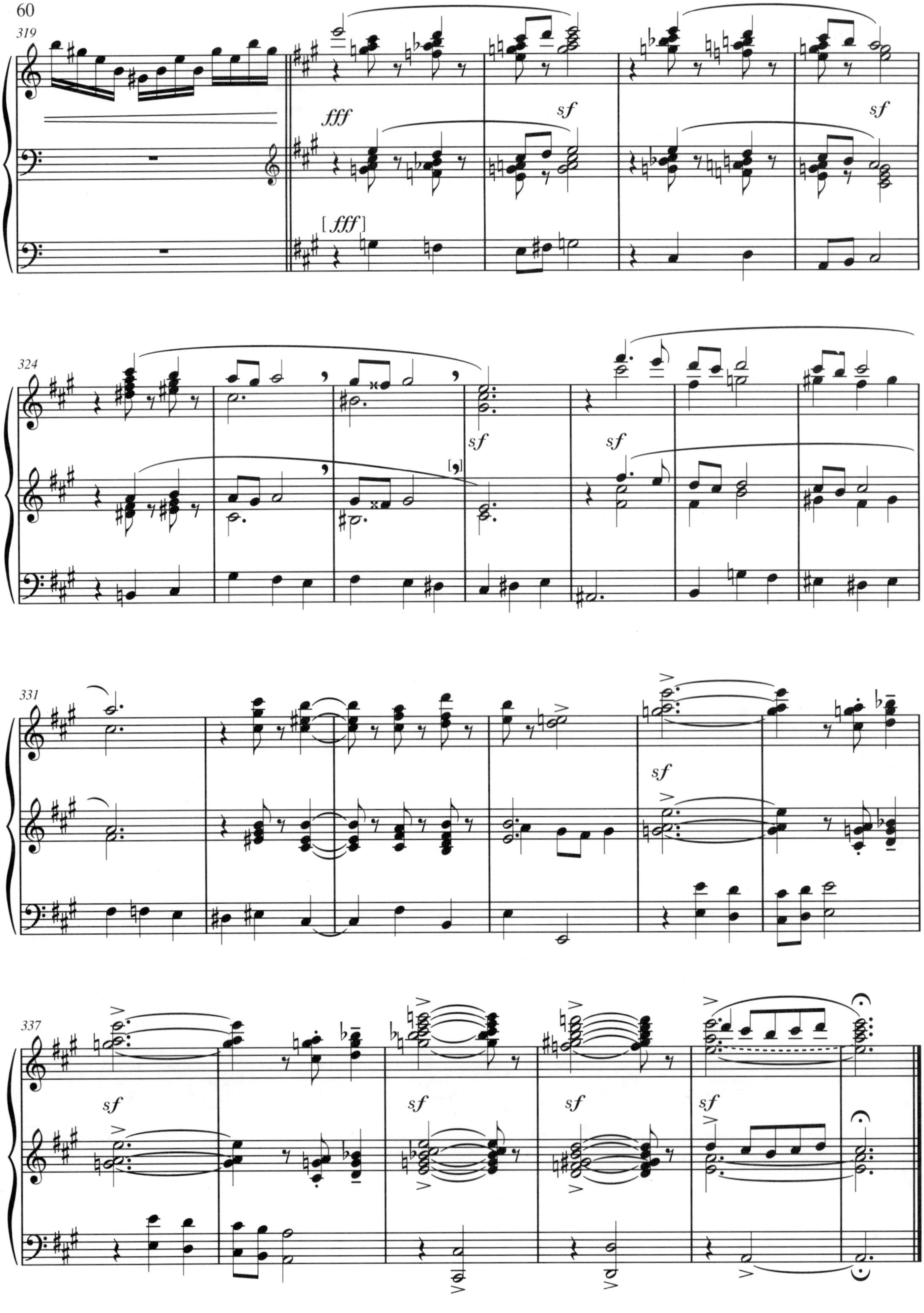
319
fff
[fff]
sf
sf
324
[,]
sf
sf
331
sf
337
sf
sf
sf
sf

Appendix 1

I

Editions *B* and *B'*, Mm. 160–68*
Emend-1 sketch, Mm. 161–68

*Editions *B* and *B'*, m. 160 = edition *E*, m. 160.

Appendix 2

IV

Version *B/B′*

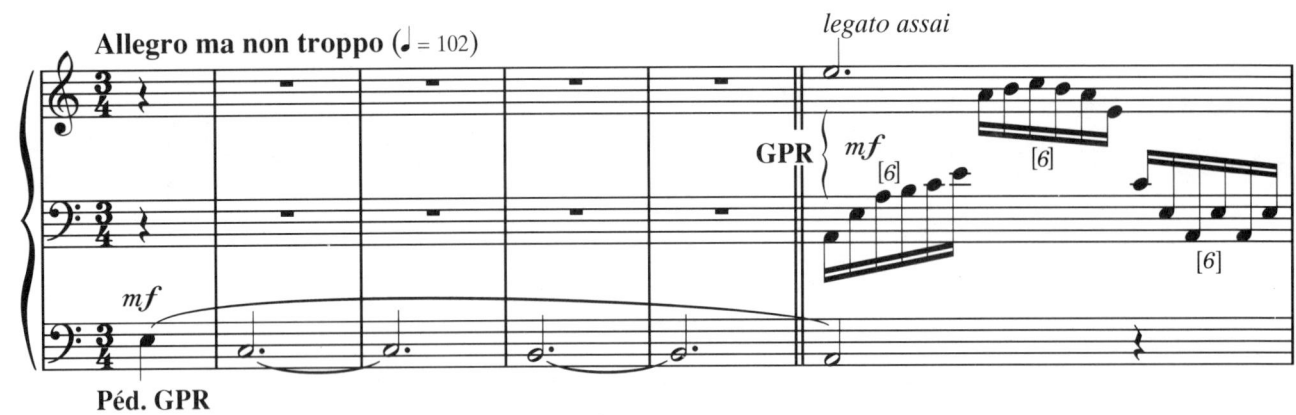

Grand orgue: Gambes 8', Flûtes 8'
Positif: Gambes 8', Flûtes 8'
Récit: [Gambes 8',] Voix célestes
Pédale: Basses 16', 8'

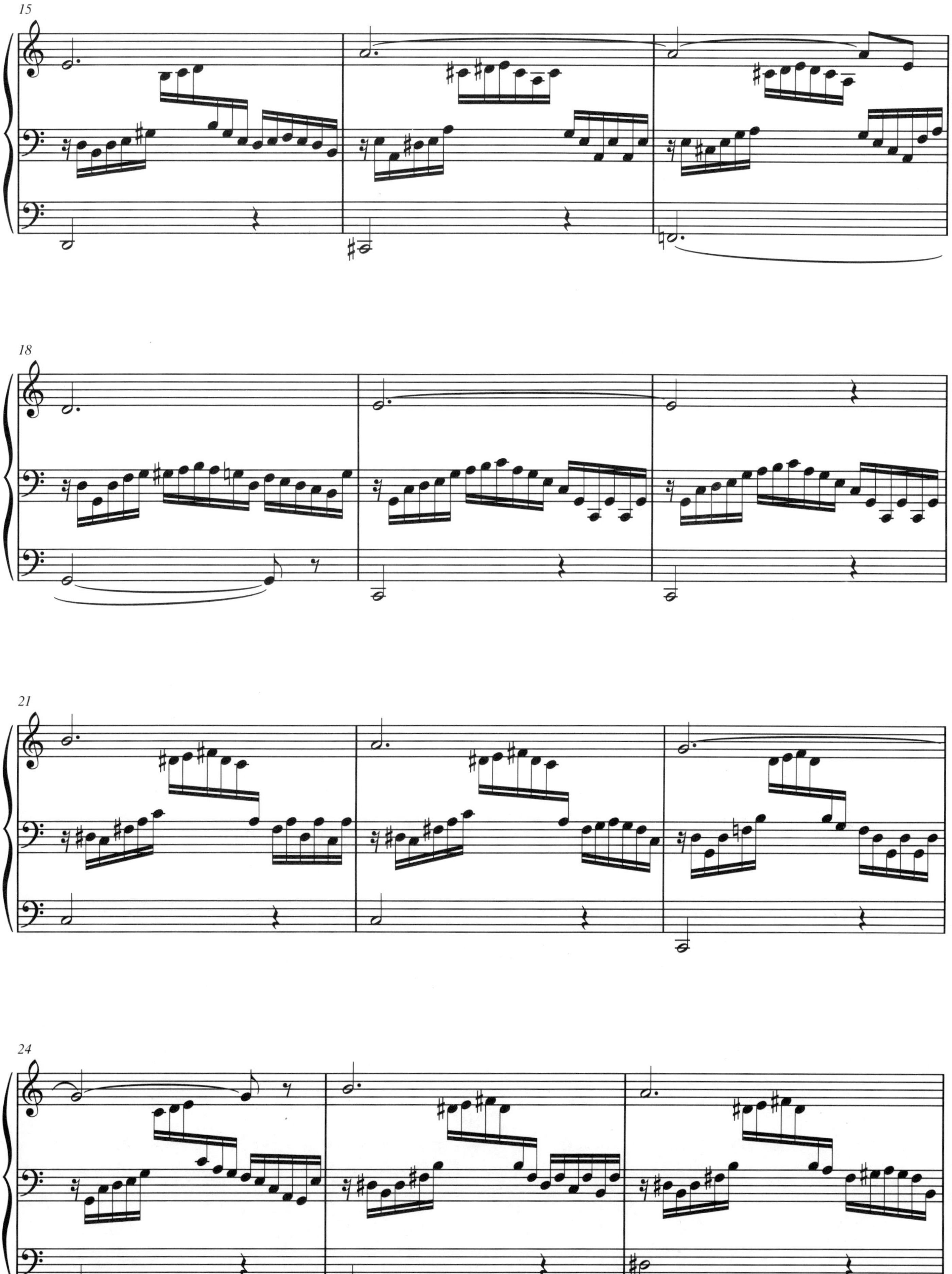
15
18
21
24

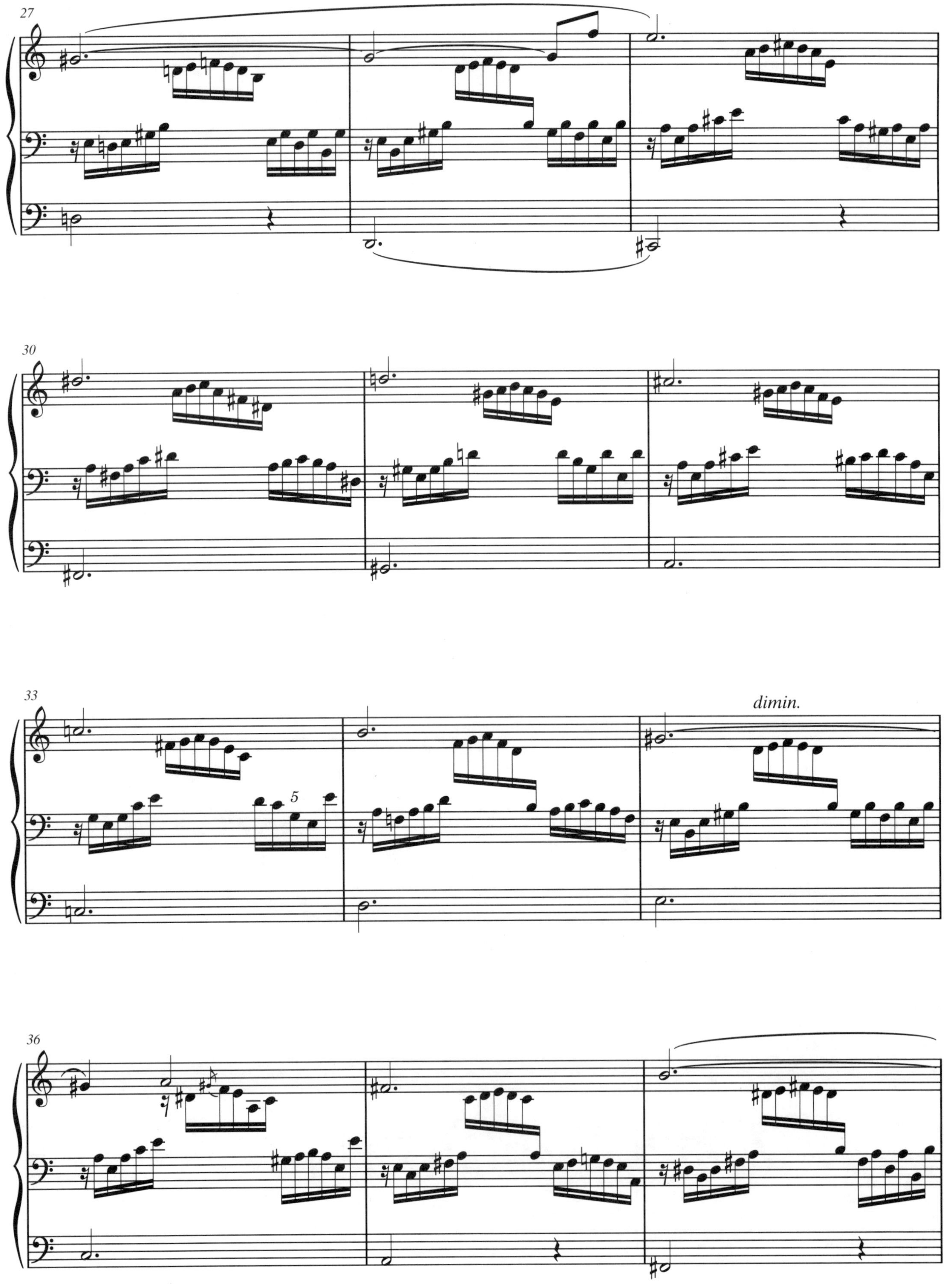
27
30
33
5
dimin.
36

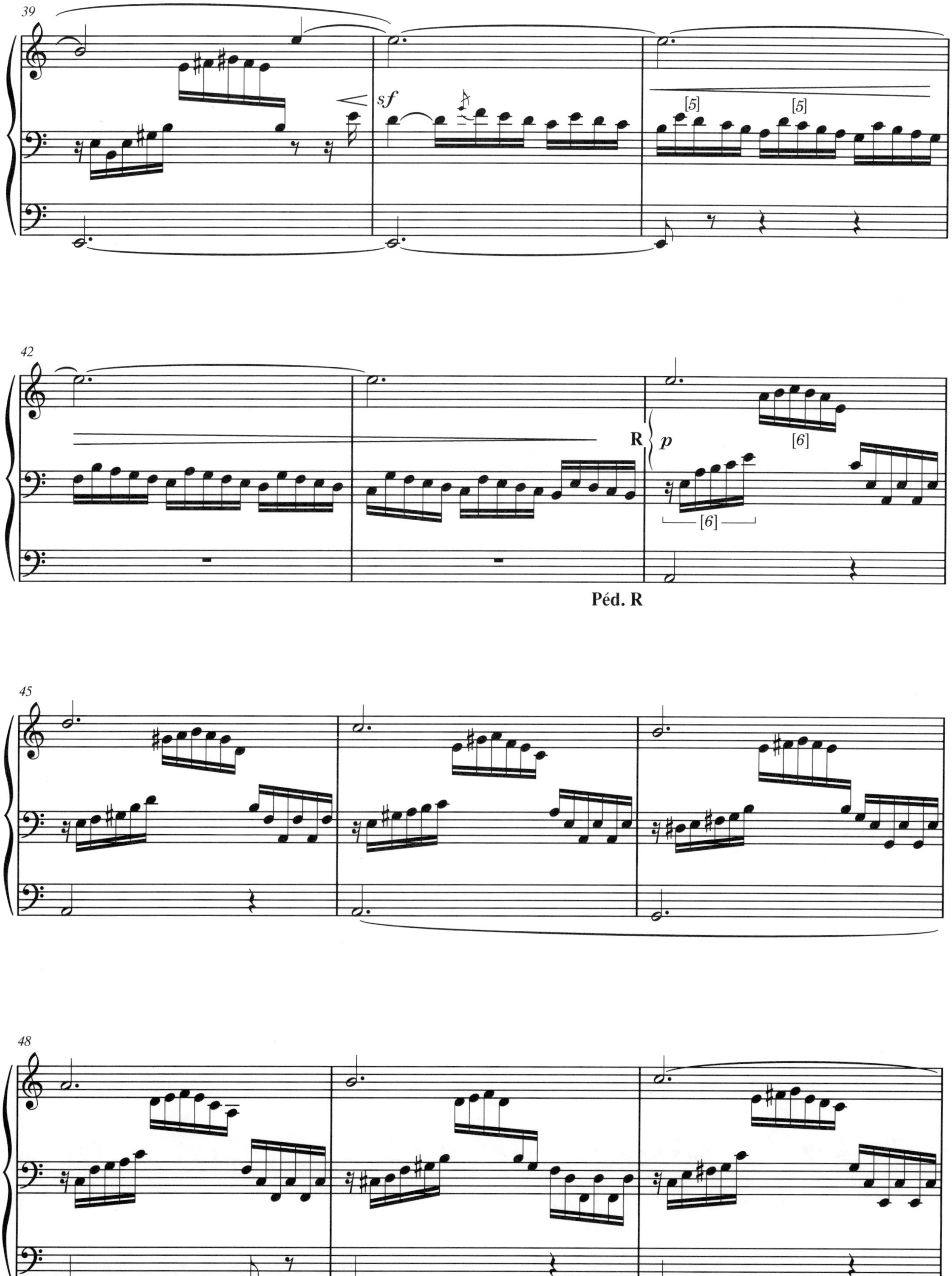
39
sf
[5]
[5]
42
R
p
[6]
[6]
Péd. R
45
48

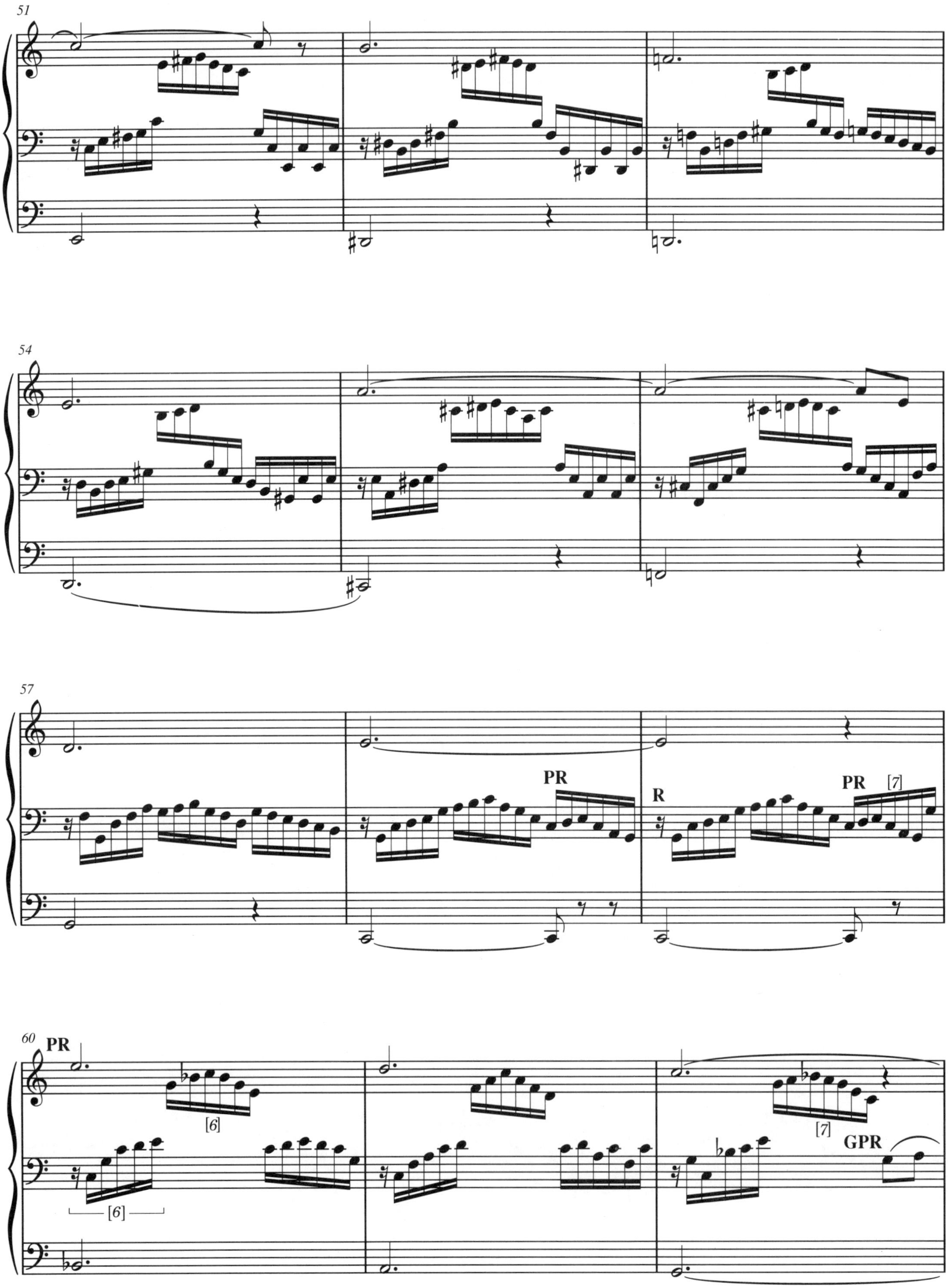
51
54
57
PR
R
PR
[7]
60
PR
[6]
[6]
[7]
GPR

67

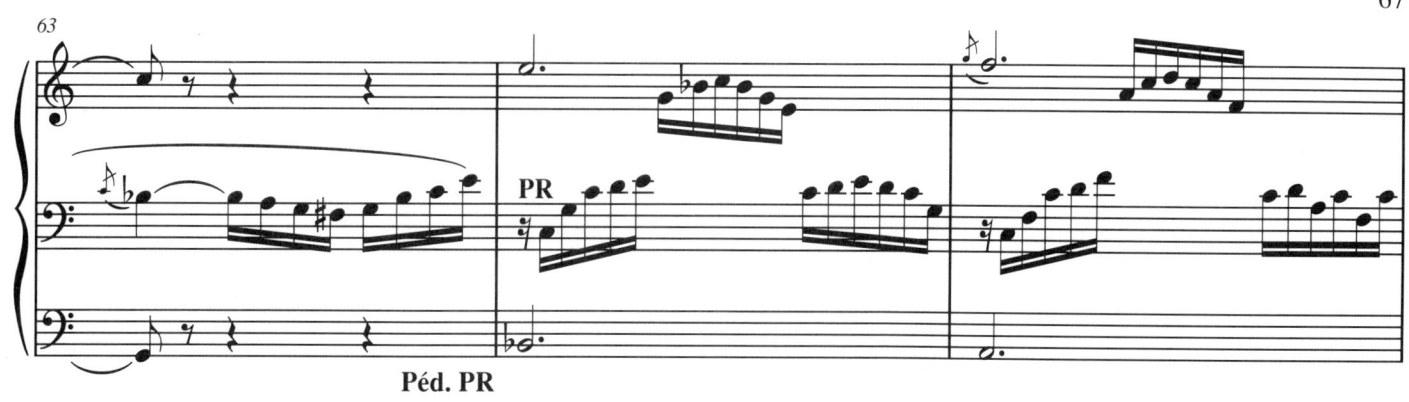

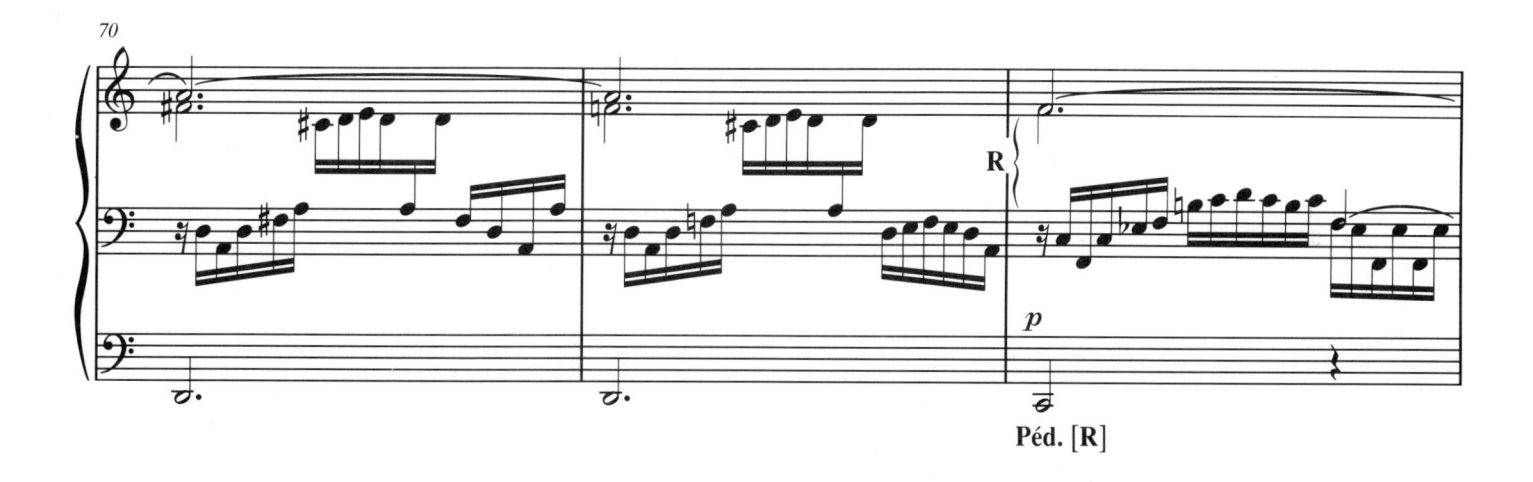

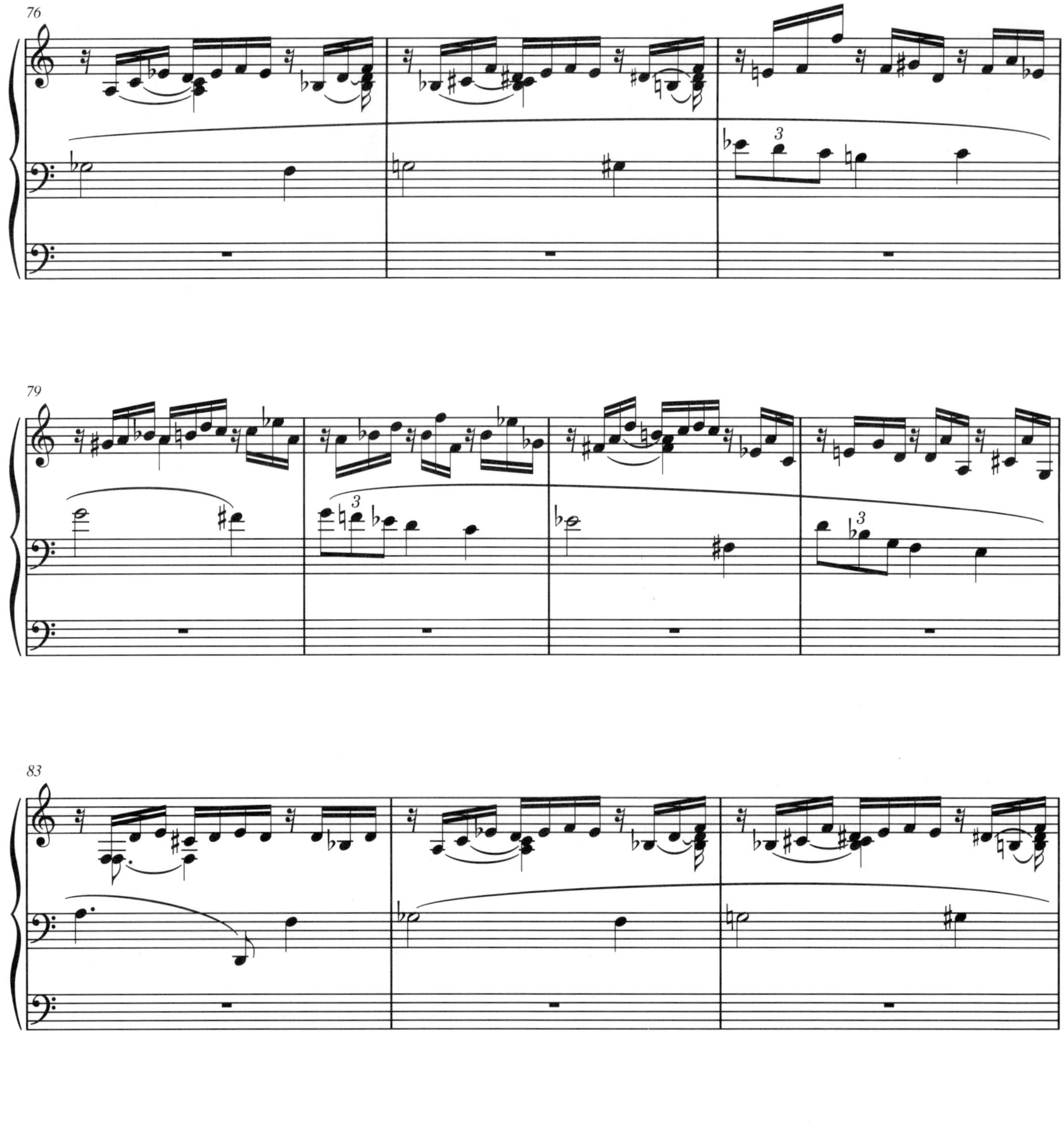
76
79
83
86
GPR
R
R
rit.

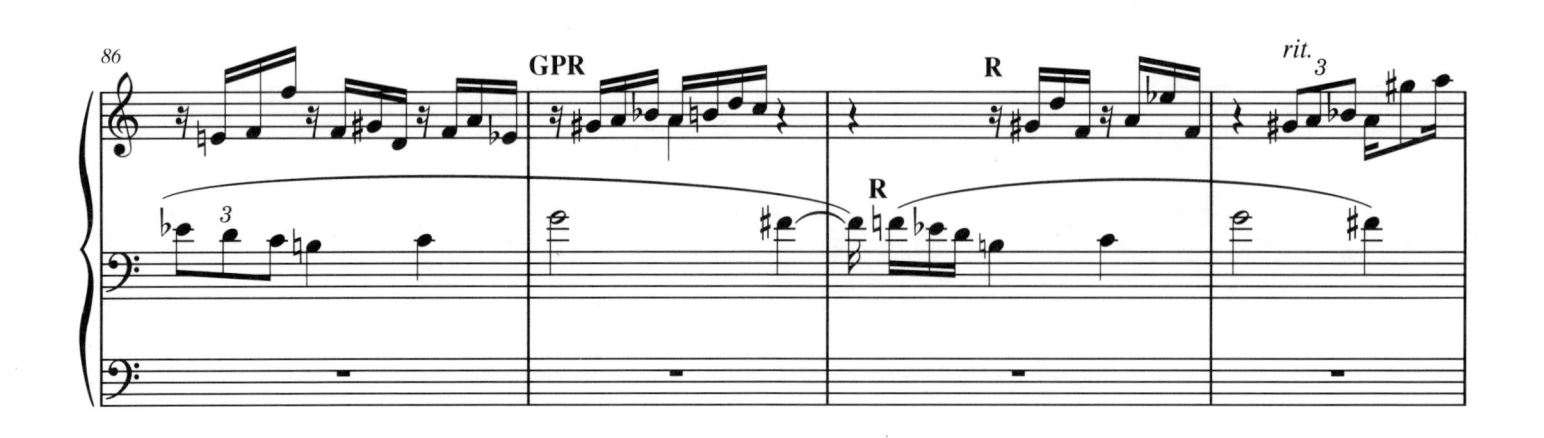

90
a tempo
R
a piacere
GPR
f
Péd. R
94
a tempo
R
[6]
5
pp
97
100
GPR
PR
[3]
p
poco a poco cresc.

70

119
PR
GPR
pp
f
GPR
Péd. R
p
Péd. GPR
123
riten.
a tempo
PR
sf
pp
PR
f
Péd. R
p
127
Péd. PR
131
Péd. GPR
f

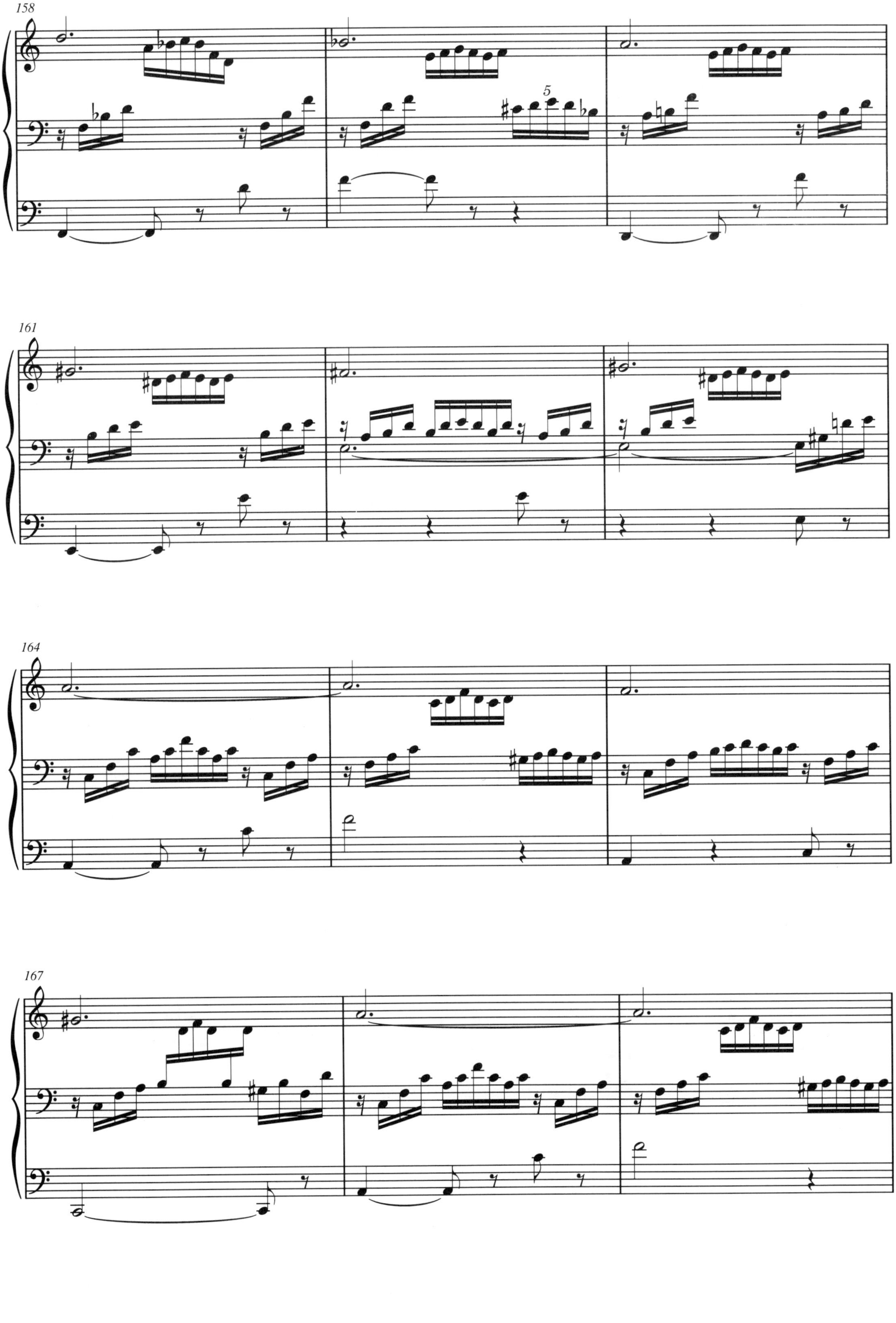
158
5
161
164
167

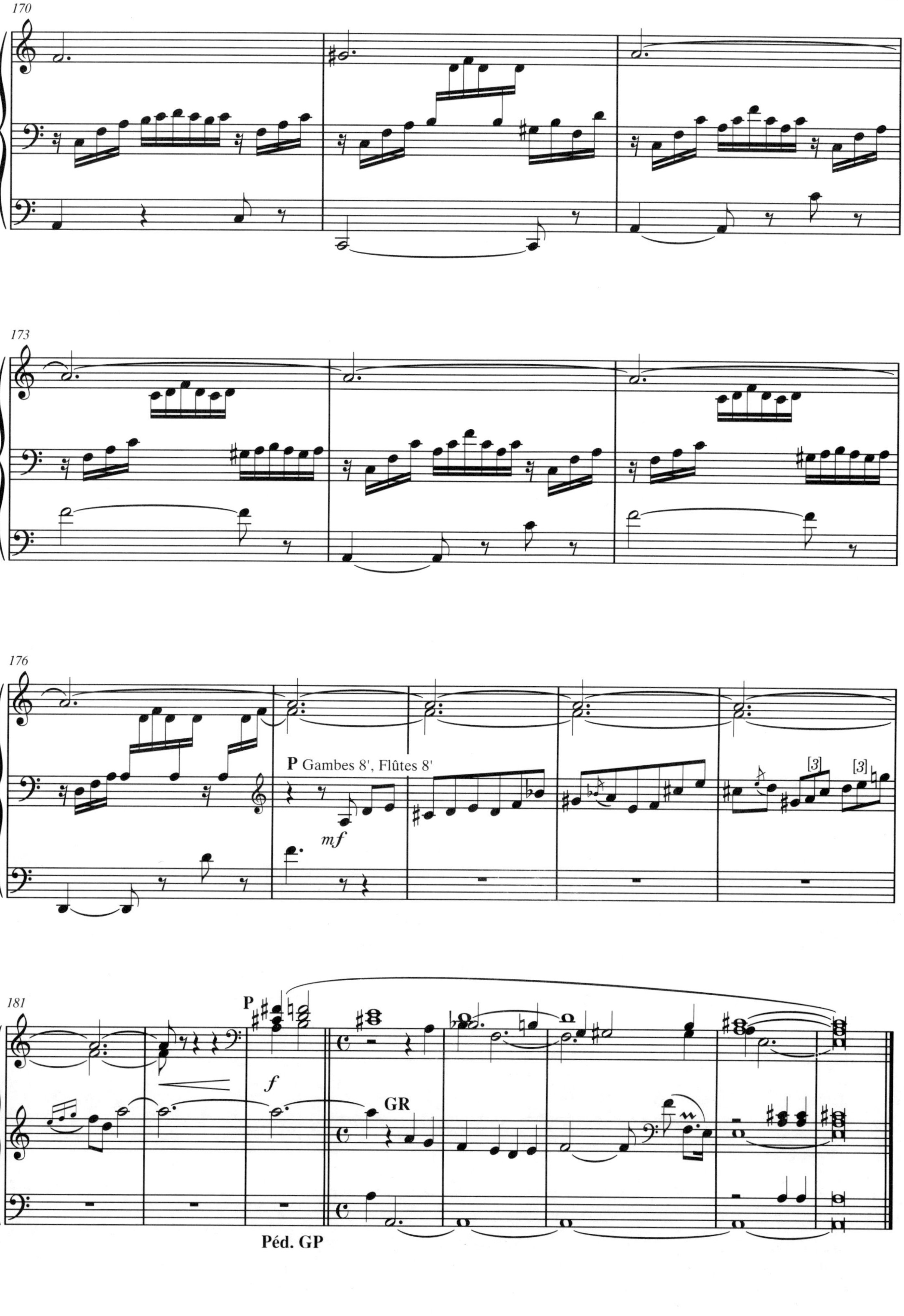
170
173
176
P Gambes 8', Flûtes 8'
mf
[3]
[3]
181
P
f
GR
Péd. GP

Appendix 3
IV

Edition C, Mm. 108–32*

*Edition C, m. 108 = edition E, m. 108; edition C, m. 132 = edition E, m. 132.

120
GPR
124
poco meno vivo, a piacere
6
6
3
128
a tempo
p
130
rit.
a tempo
pp
PR
pp

Appendix 4

V

Grand orgue: Fonds 16', 8', 4'
Positif: Gambes 8', Flûtes 8'
Récit: Voix Humaine 8' [Tremblant]
Pédale: Basses 16', 8'

Editions *B* and *B'*

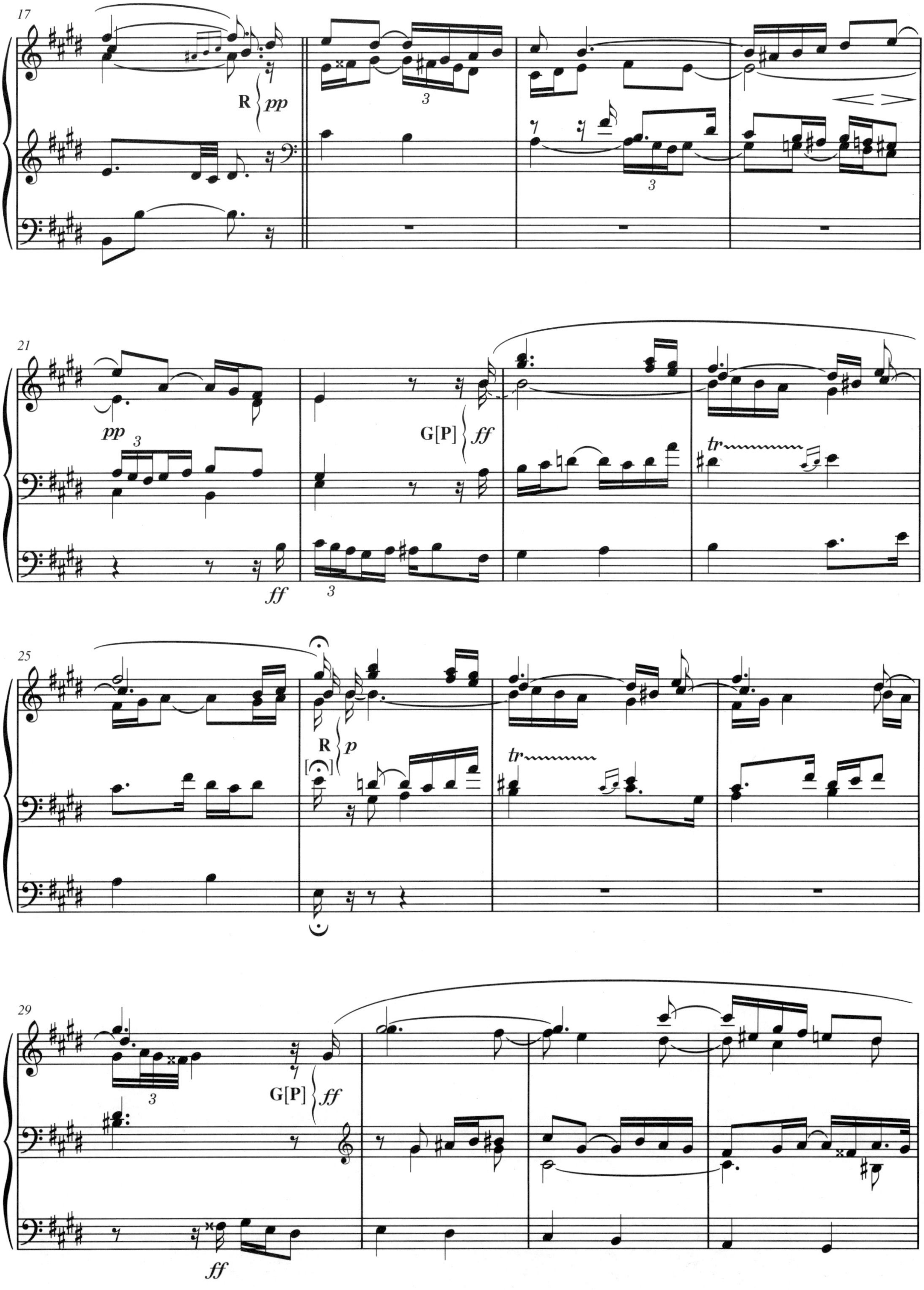
17
R pp
3
21
pp
G[P] ff
ff
tr
25
R p
tr
29
G[P] ff
ff

33
G
R
mf
f
B:
G[P]
P
mf
B':

37
R
rit.
G Flûte 8' Solo
pp
B:
dimin.
Péd. Solo
P
riten.
G Flûte 8' Solo
R
B':
sf
pp
Péd. Solo
pp

a tempo
41
P
46
più f
(R Flûte 4' solo)
Péd. P
51
R
G
56
rit.
a tempo
P
sf
Péd. GP

Appendix 5

V

Edition C, Mm. 38–50*

*Edition C, m. 38 = version C'/D/E, m. 38; edition C, m. 50 = version C'/D/E, m. 50.

Appendix 6
VI. Finale

Version *B/B′*, Mm. 235–305*

*Version *B/B′*, m. 235 = version *C′/D/E*, m. 235.

84

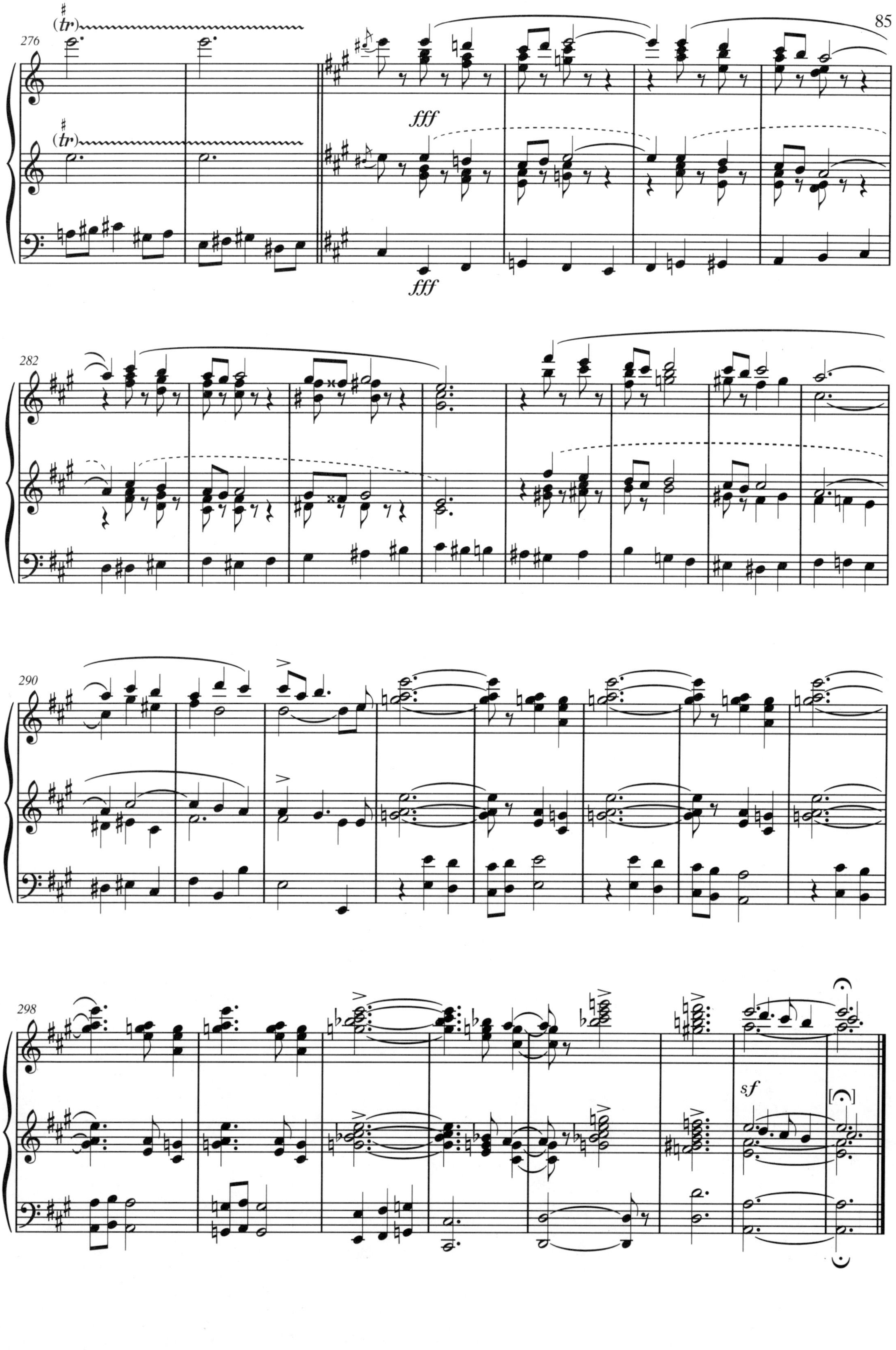
276
(tr)
(tr)
fff
fff
282
290
298
sf
[𝄐]